AGENT OF CHANGE

"If you want a strong, positive 'jump start' to your professional and personal lives, then John Murphy's books *Agent of Change* and *Reinvent Yourself* are must reads! These books penetrate right to the core of principle-centered leadership and proactive change management. I highly recommend both of them to anyone looking to lead a more fulfilling life. John Murphy is a winner—and so are his books!"

— *Ed Robertson, Brig. General, (Ret.),*
United States Air Force

"You must and will change. This book will help you do it properly."

— *Richard M. DeVos, Co-founder, Amway Corporation,*
Author, Compassionate Capitalism

"The ability to change and adapt in today's world is critical to the success and survival of any business. John Murphy's book, *Agent of Change*, does an outstanding job detailing how we can lead people and organizations through change. I highly recommend this book to anyone desiring to improve their personal leadership skills."

— *Peter F. Secchia, Chairman, Universal Forest Products, Inc.*
Former U.S. Ambassador to Italy

"The content in this book is excellent. The message that it conveys should be heard by every manager and would-be leader. I found myself wishing I had read it twenty years ago."

— *Thomas D. Gleason, Retired Chairman and CEO,*
Wolverine World Wide, Inc.

"John Murphy's *Agent of Change* applies to <u>all</u> organizations. This book speaks directly to all those seeking to create high-performance work environments. Highly readable. Highly applicable. Highly recommended."

—*Michael J. Brennan, President,*
Heart of West Michigan United Way

Leading A Cultural Revolution

"In the ten years since I started my business, I have read many business books. Without a doubt, *Pulling Together* and *Agent of Change* are two of the best! In our industry, teamwork is critical. John's books gave me practical ideas and examples I could use immediately to reinforce the teamwork concept and increase our productivity amidst the chaos of our fast paced technology business. Thanks for writing these terrific books! I look forward to the next one!!"

— Jeanne A. Englehart, CEO/President,
Productivity Point International

"In *Agent of Change,* John Murphy successfully demonstrates the power of organizational change without turning away from the difficulties encountered when long-term, key employees do not buy into the changes. If your organization is looking at or going through the "reengineering" process, this book is a must read!"

—Mark Peters, President, Butterball Farms, Inc.

"*Agent of Change* is a remarkable book. While the subject matter is about change through management systems, the principles involved transcend its setting. The ideas John Murphy presents speak as powerfully to interpersonal relationships and volunteer organizations such as the Church as to becoming an agent of change within a business environment. I read it eagerly and have passed on copies to my friends. I recommend it highly."

— Rev. Gary T. Haller, First Church

"John Murphy's *Agent of Change* is timely, provocative and easy reading for the busy executive. Anyone who is a leader or manager of people should read this book."

— Mark A. Tabit, Vice President,
Regional Sales Manager, Prudential Securities, Inc.

Also by John Murphy

Pulling Together: The Power of Teamwork

Reinvent Yourself: A Lesson in Personal Leadership

Get A Real Life: A Lesson in Personal Empowerment

The Eight Disciplines: An Enticing Look Into Your Personality

Pulling Together: The 17 Principles of Effective Teamwork

Think Change: Adapt and Thrive, or Fall Behind

Agent of Change

AGENT OF CHANGE

Leading A Cultural Revolution

by John Murphy

VENTURE MANAGEMENT CONSULTANTS, INC.
Grand Rapids, MI

AGENT OF CHANGE: LEADING A CULTURAL REVOLUTION

Copyright © 1994, 1999 by John J. Murphy

Revised edition 1999

All rights reserved. No part of this book may be reproduced or utilized in any form or by any means, electronic or mechanical, including photocopying, recording, or by any information storage and retrieval system, without the written permission of the publisher.

For more information on the concepts presented in this book or to order additional copies, please write Venture Management Consultants, Inc., P.O. Box 6651, Grand Rapids, MI 49516, or call (616) 942-2525 or 1-800-942-1120.

Library of Congress Cataloging in Publication Data

Catalog Number: 94-61008

ISBN: 0-9639013-5-4

Cover design by John Massey, 2131 N. Cleveland, Chicago, IL 60614

Pre-print production by Gremel Communications, Inc.

Printed in the United States of America

Murphy, John J., 1960-

   Agent of Change: Leading A Cultural Revolution

To leaders everywhere looking to make the world a better place.

Agent of Change

A WORD TO THE READER

While the characters in this story are fictitious, the relationships and the storyline are based on real life experiences. By creating an opportunity for you to listen in on and observe these characters in action, I hope to strengthen your understanding of the change process and enhance your effectiveness as a leader of change.

Jordan McKay, for whom this book is titled, is actually a combination of several people who have personally enriched my life and served as empowering mentors. Jordan's purpose is to give us a benchmark to think about and to learn from. Like the other characters, he is not real. Rather, he is an *ideal* for people to strive for. While no one is perfect, Jordan at least offers us a model to consider in managing, and measuring, our own behavior in an optimal and life-fulfilling manner. As you will find out, Jordan has had to learn this in a painful way.

Like any effective change agent, Jordan begins a chain reaction - teaching and inspiring others to become "agents of change," as well. He understands that in order to affect real change, he has to build a constituency of proactive leaders. No one can do it alone. He also understands that managing *to* change, rather than simply managing change, is the only way to transform a stagnant environment into a culture of high performance teamwork. Therefore, he not only teaches his constituency the difference, but he inspires them to do something about it. It is here that we distinguish the true change agent from the all too familiar crisis manager.

INTRODUCTION

T hings had to change. My gut assured me of that. At first, I tried to deny it. After all, the company was stable. Our margins were respectable. We were expanding into some new product lines. My boss at Corporate wasn't demanding anything unusual. And, unlike a lot of other companies, we weren't having to lay anybody off. The easiest thing to do would have been to leave things as they were.

But somehow I couldn't ignore my intuition. Things had to change and deep down I knew it. We weren't quick enough in responding to our customers' needs. We made promises we couldn't keep. We missed deadlines. We made careless errors. And, most importantly, many of our people acted as if they really didn't give a damn.

So my predicament was this - How was I to inspire change under these conditions? It would have been one thing if business results were awful and people's jobs were in jeopardy. Then, I might realistically expect a greater sense of urgency. We are all trained to respond to crises. But how was I to motivate my people to think differently when, in their minds, we were already successful? And how was I to convince my boss that things needed to change radically when, in his mind, we were doing just fine. If I only had a dollar for every time I heard that asinine statement, "If it ain't broke, don't fix it."

First, I tried to use logic.

"Be objective," I would hear myself say. "Argue the facts. Give people examples of other once stable companies that are now nothing more than historical statistics. Create your own crisis!" Then I would look around the conference table at a dozen frozen faces with skeptical eyeballs darting nervously about. Obviously, there was more to leading a successful transition than throwing logic at people. Sure I could have tried to force the issue, but if I was to really inspire *proactive* change, I had to learn to capture their hearts, as well as their minds.

So this is where my story begins. My name is Jack MacDonald. My birth certificate proves that I am 46-years old, but by looking at me, you might argue it's missing a few years. I grew up in a manufacturing plant and it's undoubtably taken its toll on me. My father insisted that I go to college - which I did - but my real passion has always been making things, not studying them.

I don't normally talk about heart and feeling in my line of work. In fact, I avoid it. As the general manager of a six-hundred person manufacturing facility, I am expected to produce tangible results. My boss is looking at numbers, not attitude surveys. And for that matter, I've never really had much interest in studying human behavior. It's a bit too "touchy-feely" for me.

Then I met a man who changed all of this - a man who would become my mentor. It all began when I attended a workshop he offered in Boston. In the two days that followed, the man opened my mind. It didn't hit me right away. In fact, it took several months before I appreciated the wisdom in his words. But the seeds he had planted inevitably took root, and the process of change began its course. This consultant was clearly an Agent of Change - a master of the process.

In looking back, I now realize the source of his power. He did not tell me answers. He helped me discover truths. He did not force his point of view. He simply enriched mine. He did not seek to control me. Rather, he sought to empower me. In all of the courses and seminars I've ever attended, never have I gained so much as I have from this one powerful man - and, as you can probably guess, I am not an easy person to please.

What follows is my story. It is the story of the person who changed my life and left a legacy behind in my organization. First, he helped us to *survive*. We would not have been competitive in today's global marketplace if we had not initiated our proactive, ongoing change process when we did. Second, he helped us to *thrive*. As we learned to accept change as the norm, rather than the exception, we discovered hundreds of opportunities to utilize our resources in more productive ways. This not only enriched our people, but our pocketbooks, as well.

Finally, he helped me discover the real power in balance. He showed me how linking work with play enriches the soul. He taught me that, in order to gain power, one must empower others. And in order to become rich, one must enrich others. His powerful insights even seeped through to my family life, bringing all of us closer together and moving us in a more fulfilling direction. It is these insights, and many more, that I now wish to share with you.

Please welcome the Agent of Change.

PART I

Know Your Purpose

CHAPTER 1

"Well, the first thing I would do is talk with some of the people on the front line," the man says.

"Why would you start there?"

"Because if you're going to reengineer your company to create a high performance work environment, you better pay damn close attention to what your producers think."

"What about my management team?" I ask, a little too loudly. Several heads turn at a nearby table. The small French cafe we selected for our rendezvous brews excellent coffee but leaves little room for privacy. I drop my voice down a few decibels. "You're suggesting that my managers aren't producers?"

"You tell me." The man speaks with a serious but non-threatening tone. "What exactly do they produce?"

I start to say something and then catch myself. Here I am thinking we are going to have a light conversation about some management training, and I wind up being grilled with profound philosophical inquiries.

"Try looking at it this way," the man suggests, holding up five fingers. "Given I have the information, the training, the resources, the authority and the accountability to perform my job, what do I need a boss for?"

"Support, I suppose."

"And what else?"

"Vision. Direction. Coordination. Guidance. Inspiration." I pause.

"Can we call that leadership?" the man asks.

"Yeah, I'll buy that."

"Good." He leans forward in his chair. "And can we agree that leadership is a *service?*"

Again, I offer my consent.

"So tell me, how do you measure the quality of this service?"

I start laughing.

"I suppose you have to ask the people who are using it." The man has an interesting way of making his point. He knew that I knew the answer.

"Besides, by first talking with the people on the front line, I get a better read on who in management is bullshitting me." The man smiles and sips his coffee.

I begin wondering whether to trust this guy or make up some excuse to leave. But what if he's just testing me? Maybe he's trying to figure out how committed I am to the whole change process. Maybe he's the one prepared to walk away. Imagine that - a selective consultant.

"But what if the people on the front line don't have the information and training and resources and authority and accountability to perform their jobs? Wouldn't that mean that management has to..." I stop.

"To what? Manage all of their problems for them? Or attempt to control them?"

Again, I start to say something but catch myself. That's exactly the problem we have now. Instead of preparing people to manage themselves, we are trying to manage everything for them. No wonder I feel like I'm aging prematurely. Maybe I'm the friggin' bottleneck.

"Remember something, Jack. *When it comes to human*

relationships, control is nothing but an illusion." The man leans forward. "Concentrate on *commitment,* not on *control.*"

"I suppose you're right."

"Tell me something else," the man continues. "Is it a high performance work environment you're after?"

I nod. That's how this whole thing got started. I intend to run the best division in the entire corporation.

"And how would you describe a high performance work environment?"

"It's like you said in your workshop," I reply. "It's an environment whereby the producers have everything they need, including authority and accountability, to get their work done efficiently and effectively."

"And...?"

"And it's an environment where people work interdependently as a team and focus only on things that matter."

"That's right. You never want to confuse *activity* with *productivity.*" He sips his coffee. "Anything else?"

"Yeah, it's also an environment where the emphasis is placed on the processes, or the relationship between tasks, rather than on the individual tasks themselves."

"I'm impressed."

"And it's an environment where people are continuously learning and applying themselves."

"Either you have an excellent memory, Jack, or you take great notes."

"You were very clear on that topic."

The man smiles.

"And what does it take to create this kind of culture?"

"High performance leadership."

"There you go." The man leans forward. "So tell me, why don't you measure the quality of your leadership? Isn't it important to you?"

The man won't let up. I hesitate, but not long enough.

"Of course it's important to us. But our people do as they're told." Again, a few heads turn. I whisper. "Besides, we have job descriptions and a labor agreement that spell out exactly what people are expected to do."

There is a long pause. Finally, the man laughs.

"I'm afraid we're talking about two entirely different things, my friend. You are describing *agreement*. I am asking about *commitment*."

I do not respond. The man reads my mind.

"Think of it this way," he explains. "Agreement comes from the head." He taps his temple. "People agree to things everyday because they believe they have to." He sets his coffee down and rests his elbows on the table. "Commitment, on the other hand, comes from the heart. People commit because they want to."

I gaze at him without expression. My mind begins to wander.

"Consider a typical school system," he explains, drawing me back to reality. "The system requires that students attend class everyday, right?"

"Sure, that's pretty standard."

"And if they don't agree to this, they can be reprimanded." He pauses to let the analogy sink in. "Tell me, Jack, does this system elicit agreement or commitment?"

"Sounds like our attendance program," I reply. "It gets people to show up, but it doesn't get them to care."

"That's right. It focuses on control rather than on commitment. Now, wouldn't you consider it a competitive advantage to have a workforce that is committed to going beyond standard, or even raising the standards, as opposed to one agreeing only to do what they have to?"

"Absolutely."

"And how do you suppose you build this kind of commitment?"

"By servicing the producers with quality leadership."

"There you go," the man confirms. "People must be led, not managed."

"But what about the people who don't want to take responsibility and manage themselves? What am I supposed to do about them?"

"Start by holding your management team accountable for providing quality leadership and you may be surprised by how quickly the others climb on board."

"And you're suggesting I do this by measuring it?"

"Yes, I am. Measurement creates focus and accountability. With it, people know what is expected, and they have access to the score. Without it, people lose interest." The man stops and looks at me as if about to reveal a deep secret. "Remember something, Jack. *You get what you inspect, not what you expect.* If quality leadership is what you're after, you have no choice but to figure out how to define it and measure it."

The man leans back in his chair and sips his coffee. As I look at him, I find myself intrigued by his character. He doesn't look to be more than forty-five years old, but he speaks with the wisdom and maturity of a venerable sage. His athletic physique and casual dress give him an almost ageless aura, as if he could blend in with almost any crowd. He is poised and confident, yet humble and without pretense. His crystal-blue eyes speak of honesty, integrity and decency. But underneath all of that, I sense that he is intensely competitive. What makes this man tick?

"Can I ask you something?"

"Shoot," the man replies.

"What would you say is the criteria for leading people effectively? What exactly is it we should measure?"

Without saying a word, he grabs a blank index card and ballpoint pen from his shirt pocket and prepares to write.

"Let me suggest that you answer your own question with a simple exercise. First, get an image in your mind of the best boss you've ever had. Think of someone who you would personally qualify as an inspiring leader - someone who helped you achieve a level of performance even you may not have believed was possible." He pauses while I turn my mind loose on my twenty-plus years of experience.

"Got one?"

"Hold on. This exercise may not be as simple as you think." As my mind races back over the years, the man watches me intently. He probably knows that most of my bosses were nothing more than self-imposed cops - kicking butt and taking names. And the few that weren't either got into trouble or quit. Suddenly, it hits me like a bolt of lightning. I remember a guy I had for a boss when I was in my early twenties. It was only for about six months, but I would have done anything for this man. "Okay. I have one."

"Good. Now describe for me why you found this person to be such an effective leader. What was it that made the difference?"

"Well, to begin with, he made me feel important," I explain, staring out the window. "He asked me for my opinions and he considered my point of view. He kept me informed. He involved me in decisions. He gave me a sense of accomplishment." I stop for a few seconds to reflect on the image I have in my mind. "I suppose, in a nutshell, he *trusted* me. And he demonstrated his trust by giving me responsible things to do. He helped me to grow."

"And did you trust him?"

"Definitely. It was a two-way street."

"Okay. Now look at what you have just described to me." The man slides the index card across the table. "What does this tell you?"

> ** Made me feel important*
> ** Asked for my opinions*
> ** Considered my point of view*
> ** Kept me informed*
> ** Involved me in decisions*
> ** Gave me a sense of accomplishment*
> ** Trusted me*
> ** Gave me responsibility*
> ** Helped me to grow*
> ** I trusted him*

"It tells me that this boss made me feel like a winner. He instilled in me a sense of power and inner-strength. All he had to do was point me in the right direction."

"That is precisely the sign of a great leader."

I stop and think for a moment.

"But wouldn't different people have different criteria for describing a best boss?"

"Why don't you answer that question for yourself. You might be surprised." With that, the man pushes his chair away from the small oak table and stands up to leave. "I'll give you a call in a few days to follow up. For now, I have a plane to catch."

Seconds later, he is gone. The agent of change has vanished.

"What a pain in the ass," I say to myself. "The guy wasn't here thirty minutes and he already has me doing homework."

CHAPTER 2

"Hi, Honey. How was your day?" my wife asks as I walk into the kitchen. Once again, I have missed dinner.

"Well, with the exception of about thirty minutes, it was a lot like any other day," I reply, throwing my briefcase on a chair and stripping the tie from my neck. "Everyone coming to me with their problems."

"And what about the other thirty minutes?"

"I don't know," I shrug. "It was like I got slapped."

"By who? Was Wesley back in town today?"

Wesley is my boss, the president of TYPCO Manufacturing. He works out of our corporate headquarters in Boston. About twice a month, he shows up at our plant in Brockton to go over the numbers with me. Like most of my past bosses, Wesley treats people like he's wearing some kind of badge.

"No, not Wesley," I reply. "He's actually been backing off lately. As long as I keep hitting my numbers, he stays out of my face."

"Then by who?" Judy looks concerned.

"Do you remember the guy I told you about a few months ago?" I ask. "The man who conducted the workshop on high performance teamwork?"

"How could I forget?" she replies. "You talked about him for days."

"Well, I had breakfast with him this morning and now I can't get the guy off my mind."

Judy is an excellent sounding board for me. She is sensitive, objective and patient. I know I abuse this privilege from time to time, but with all the bullshit I have to put up with as G.M., I need someone who will simply listen to me once in awhile.

"So what did he say?" she asks, guiding me onto a kitchen stool and pouring me an ice cold Samuel Adams lager.

"It isn't so much what he said. It's more what he asked."

"So what did he ask?" Judy sits down beside me with a glass of Chardonnay.

"Well, he asked me things I probably should have been asking myself a long time ago. That's why I feel like I got slapped."

"So, are you upset with this man?"

"No, not at all. He isn't the one who slapped me."

"Then who did?"

"I slapped myself. All he did was prompt me to it."

"How'd he do that?"

"He did it by opening my eyes up to some things I should have been paying more attention to. I guess you could say he empowered me to slap myself."

"Sounds interesting." Judy sips her wine. "So what exactly is it you've been overlooking?"

Without saying a word, I pull the index card from my shirt pocket and gaze at it. My wife watches me intently, anxiously awaiting my reply. Finally, she can wait no longer.

"What's with the card?"

"Well, before I explain that, let me ask you to do something. First, close your eyes and get an image in your mind of the best boss you've ever had."

"That would be Margaret," Judy replies without hesitation. Margaret is her current boss over at the hospital. Judy works part-time in administration.

"It doesn't matter who it is specifically. Just get a picture of someone who you consider to be an inspiring leader."

"Okay, I'm ready."

"Now, describe for me why you consider this person to be such an effective boss." I grab a pen from my shirt pocket and prepare to write.

"Well, to begin with, she pays attention to us. She makes us feel important - like we matter." Judy pauses and sips her wine. "And she always keeps us well-informed and involved in what is going on. She leaves little room for assumption. Margaret has a very open-mind and she encourages us to speak up and share our ideas."

"Good. Anything else?"

"Yeah. She has us set goals so that we can see our accomplishments. And she allows for mistakes - as long as they're honest and we learn from them." Judy stops and looks at me. "There, how's that?"

"Great." I have now documented each of Judy's answers on the opposite side of the same index card my answers are on. I slide the card over in front of her.

Pays attention to us
Makes us feel important
Keeps us well-informed and involved
Keeps an open mind
Encourages us to speak up and share ideas
Sets goals and creates a sense of accomplishment
Allows for honest mistakes

"Now take a look at what you said about your best boss, and then look at what I said about my best boss."

Judy turns the card over and over in her hands comparing each item.

"Looks like a pattern," she says. "Both of our ideal bosses made us feel like winners."

"Do you suppose this is true of everyone?" I ask, thinking back to my homework assignment. "I mean, what if we were to ask a hundred people the same question."

"Reminds me of one of my Psych courses in college," Judy says. "Have you ever heard of Maslow's Hierarchy of Needs?"

"It sounds familiar. Doesn't that have something to do with security and self-esteem?"

"Those are two of the needs," she replies. "But there are more."

A few minutes later, Judy has not only described each of the five need levels, but she has sketched a picture of the hierarchy on a piece of scratch paper. I feel like a kid having my girlfriend help me with my homework.

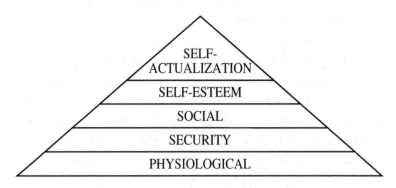

"Wow. This really has some interesting applications in the business world," I conclude, staring at the diagram in front of me.

"How's that?"

"Think about it. The paycheck aims at the physiological needs. The safety procedures and insurance policies aim at the security needs. The company picnics and T-shirts aim at the social needs - not to mention the union's activities."

"I'm sure the union takes credit for the first two levels, as well," Judy interrupts.

"I won't argue that," I continue. "But we aren't doing a damn thing in our organization to build self-esteem and help people know their purpose and achieve their potential. In fact, we're probably doing just the opposite."

"What about training? You offer all kinds of training."

"Yeah, but training only frustrates people if you don't reinforce it with action. I see it every day. We probably waste thousands of dollars every year on seminars and workshops because we don't allow people to really use what they learn."

Judy just looks at me, her soft green eyes gazing into mine. She digests the thought...

"For example, we sent every one of our employees through Statistical Process Control training two years ago. Guess what? Probably 80% of them never use it. Why? Because we don't have the systems in place to reinforce it."

Judy just listens.

"And problem-solving skills. There's a farce. We put everyone through four hours of problem-solving training a year ago. Cost us thousands of dollars. Guess who's still solving 80% of the problems? Surprise! It's Management! Why? Because we act as if everyone else in the organization is too stupid and irresponsible to solve their own problems. The accountability is in the wrong place." I take a large swig of my beer.

"Well, I'll tell you what," Judy says softly. "Margaret sure has done a lot for my self-esteem in the business world. Maybe that's why I consider her to be such an effective leader."

Suddenly, a light goes on.

"Hey, maybe that's the connection. Maybe it's managers who go beyond the physiological, security and social needs and tap the higher needs that distinguish themselves as great leaders." I pause and reflect on what I have just said. "I wonder if that's what Jordan meant when he said I might be surprised."

"Jordan? Is that the man's name?"

"Yeah, Jordan McKay."

"That's an interesting name."

"It's even more interesting when you meet the guy," I add. "He's quite a character."

"So, what exactly did Jordan suggest you do?" Judy is now determined to find out why this man has such an effect on me.

"Well, he suggested that I begin by finding out what distinguishes great leaders from everyone else."

"And then what?"

"And then I use this criteria to start measuring the quality of our leadership."

"And how do you plan to measure the quality of your leadership?"

"Just like I would any other service - by asking the people who depend on it to evaluate it?"

Judy starts laughing.

"Well, that ought to get a few people's attention." I know exactly who she is talking about, but I choose to let it slide. There is no doubt we have a few people in our organization who won't find this amusing.

I take another swig of my beer.

"I have to start somewhere."

"That's true. And I suppose if you don't measure the quality of your leadership, people might assume it isn't important to you."

Bingo. Judy hits the nail on the head. I lean over and kiss her.

"Thanks for listening."

She smiles.

"So when are you going to see Jordan again?"

"Not for a while. He just left for Washington. He's a part of some special task force commissioned by the Vice President to revitalize government. In fact, I met him on his way to the airport. I've been trying to set something up with the guy for weeks."

"Sounds like he's in demand."

"There's no doubt about that," I reply. "But you would never know it by talking to him."

"What do you mean?"

"He's humble," I reply, standing up and walking over to the kitchen sink. "And he's genuine. There's no pretense about him."

"That's refreshing," Judy says.

"Yeah. But I still can't figure the guy out. There's something else..."

Judy looks at me.

"I'd like to meet him someday."

"Hopefully, you will. I'm sure you'd like him."

"So what do you plan to do about dinner?"

"I'll just fix myself a sandwich. Sorry I was late." Judy's heard the words a thousand times before.

"Well, maybe things will finally start to change."

I do not reply for fear of leaving Judy with yet another broken promise. But this time, I sense she might be right.

"By the way," Judy adds. "You might want to go upstairs and talk to Kevin. You aren't the only one who's had a rough day."

CHAPTER 3

"You okay?" I ask, tapping lightly on my son's door. He's sitting at his desk with his back to me.

"I'm fine," the boy replies without looking up.

Kevin is fifteen going on twenty. He is a good student and a fine athlete. And, like most teenagers, he insists he knows everything.

"Want to tell me about your day?" I ask, walking into the room.

"Not right now," he replies. He continues to stare at the mathbook in front of him.

"Got a lot of homework?" I persist.

"Yeah. Enough."

"Can I help?"

"No thanks, Dad."

"Sorry I couldn't make your basketball game?"

"That's okay," he replies. "You're a busy guy."

"Did you kick some butt?"

"Actually, we got our butts kicked," he replies after a long pause.

"What happened?" I sit down on the corner of Kevin's bed. He still hasn't looked up.

"Our coach doesn't know what he's doing."

"Oh. So it's the coach's fault?"

It was the wrong thing to say. The boy immediately shuts down.

"I figured you would side with him," he mumbles.

"Hey, hold on. I'm not siding with anyone." I immediately recognize my mistake and try to recover. I remember an analogy Jordan had used in his workshop. Think of leadership like working with a piece of string. Push it and it piles up in front of you. Pull it and it will follow you anywhere. I try pulling. "So what do you suppose your coach is doing wrong?"

The boy begins to open back up.

"For one thing, he doesn't know how to use our strengths to offset our weaknesses."

"What do you mean?"

"He just doesn't know how to use us right. He's got people in the wrong positions and everyone on the team knows it."

"Everyone but the coach?"

The boy laughs.

"Yeah, everyone but the coach."

"What else is he doing wrong?"

"He doesn't know how to improvise."

"Hmmm. And I suppose knowing how to improvise is pretty important in a game like basketball."

"You better believe it."

"So why is improvisation so important?"

"Because things are always changing, Dad," Kevin spins around in his chair and looks at me. He still has the boyish face of a young teen, but he speaks with confidence. His mother has trained him well. "Basketball is a game where you have to think on your feet. You have to be quick. You have to cover for one another. There is no predictability to the game.

"In other words, you have to work as a team."

"Exactly," the boy replies. "You have to put the team's

interests in front of your own. It's the only way to win."

"And your team has a problem with this?" Meanwhile, I admit to myself that Kevin's team isn't the only one suffering from a lack of teamwork in the face of constant change.

"Yeah, we have a big problem with this. Some of the guys only care about themselves. It's like they're competing with one another instead of the other team."

"Sounds like a sure way to lose."

"We've proven that."

"So what is your coach doing about this?"

"That's just it, Dad. The man isn't doing anything. I don't think he even has a clue on what teamwork is all about."

"How do you figure?" I wonder aloud. "Wouldn't a basketball coach be required to understand the principles of teamwork?"

"That's what you would think," Kevin replies. "But to me it's no different than having a teacher who doesn't know anything about how to motivate a kid to learn."

My heart sinks into my stomach. I wonder how many people we have in TYPCO management who don't know how to inspire high performance teamwork - including me!

"How do you suppose these teachers and coaches get into these positions?" I ask.

"Why all the questions, Dad? You feeling okay?"

I'm not surprised by the boy's reaction. After all, he's used to my old-fashioned command and control attitude.

"I'm fine, Kevin," I confirm with a smile.

My son is not convinced.

"I guess I just haven't been listening to your point of view enough lately. And I apologize."

Kevin suddenly looks at me like I'm his long lost hero. I pick up a miniature basketball laying beside the bed and start tossing it from one hand to the other.

"Well, I suppose they get into the positions because the people who hire them don't have their priorities straight."

I start to laugh - painfully.

"Like the ability to get students and athletes to focus on the things that matter most?"

"Yeah. It's like a lot of teachers and coaches don't even care about what happens to us. They don't prepare us for the real world. They just go through the motions and cover their own butts."

And we end up hiring them, I think to myself.

"Tell me something, Kevin. Do you have any really great teachers."

"Yeah, I have one who I would put in that category - Ms. Marks."

"Why do you consider Ms. Marks so special?"

"She's different. She takes a real interest in what is important to me and to my future. She makes me feel important, like I matter. She places less emphasis on grades and more emphasis on the potential I have as a person."

"Maslow," I say softly, thinking aloud.

"What?"

"Nothing. I was just thinking aloud. So what about your basketball coach? How would you describe him?"

"Like a dictator." Kevin doesn't hesitate for a second. "He treats us like we're a bunch of idiots."

"What about his strategy to pull you guys together as a team?"

"That's just it, Dad." The boy looks me straight in the eyes. "I don't think he has a strategy. We don't know what he's thinking."

"What do you mean by that?"

"We just know we're supposed to try to win," Kevin explains. "Other than that, it's total chaos. There's nothing holding us together."

"Sounds a little bit like the way things are at the plant." I mumble.

"Well, I wouldn't know about that. But it's no fun losing, especially when you're giving it your all."

"So, you're saying that you have guys committed to winning but they don't have a strategy in place to help them accomplish this?"

"Do you know anyone committed to losing, Dad?"

"No, but I know some people who aren't committed at all."

Kevin is now looking directly at me.

"And why do you suppose they aren't committed?"

All of a sudden, I feel like I'm back sitting with Jordan. That's a damn good question. Every human being has a heart.

"You tell me," I pull.

"I think it's because they don't see any reason why they should be. They've given up. We have guys like that on the team right now. And it's getting worse."

"Do you think your coach knows this?"

"I don't know. He doesn't pay much attention to what the players think."

Suddenly, I remember something Jordan had said. If you really want to create a high performance work environment, you better pay damn close attention to what your producers think.

"Tell me something, Kevin. Do you think your team could come up with a winning strategy if the players were more involved in the planning process?"

"It sure wouldn't hurt," he replies. "After all, we're the ones out on the floor. Don't you think our opinion might help?"

"So why doesn't your coach ask for it?" Somehow, I already know the answer.

"Ego," the boy says without hesitation. "He just looks at us like we're a bunch of know-nothing kids. He's the coach. He's the boss. We're just a bunch of puppets."

"Sounds like a losing strategy to me." I now have a knot in my stomach. We're making the same damn mistake at TYPCO.

"Tell me something, Dad." Kevin is now miles away from his math homework. "How do you suppose it makes a person feel when they are treated like they don't have a brain in their head."

Little does Kevin know that he is now rubbing salt in my wounds.

"I imagine it hurts."

"It does more than that. It makes you feel like you don't matter. It makes you feel like a loser."

"Do you feel like a loser, Kevin?"

"Sometimes."

I feel like I've just been zapped with a ray gun.

"Do I treat you like you don't matter?"

The boy looks at me as if determining whether or not to trust me. He takes the risk.

"Sometimes." He speaks the truth.

"What do I do that makes you feel that way?"

He is now looking at the floor with his elbows on his knees. He looks like someone sitting on the bench. I feel his pain.

"You don't pay attention to what's important to me, for one thing," he says quietly. "Your mind is always someplace else. And Kathleen feels the same way." Kathleen is my eleven year old daughter.

Suddenly I remember a term Jordan had used in his workshop. The term was *Perception Warp*. He defined it as a situation where one person's perception of something is different than another person's perception of the same thing. And here I am suffering from Perception Warp with my own son. My perception is that he and his sister and his mother come first in my life. His perception is just the opposite. He thinks that he comes at the end of the line. And it's *his* perception that determines his commitment.

"So you feel like you come at the end of the line?" I acknowledge that I understand him.

"When is the last time you came to one of my games?" he replies. "Or one of Kathleen's concerts?"

"You're right, son. I have let you down. I'm sorry."

He's heard that before.

"What would you say if I started attending more of your games - no ifs, ands or buts?"

"That would be nice," he replies with an 'I'll believe it when I see it' look on his face. "But promise me you won't start screaming at me from the stands like some of the other fathers do. That's the only thing that could be worse."

"Don't worry, Kevin. I won't embarrass you."

"You want another example?"

I swallow hard.

"Yeah, I suppose I can take it."

"You don't treat me like I can make a responsible decision for myself. How am I ever supposed to learn how to make responsible decisions if you never give me the chance?" Suddenly, it occurs to me. I'm not just suffering from an employee dependency syndrome at work. I have the same problem at home. I am not preparing my son to make responsible decisions for himself. I'm trying to make all of them for him.

"I guess I just don't want you to get hurt."

"In the short-run or the long-run?" the boy asks.

Damn. This kid is sharp. Where the hell have I been?

"In the short-run *and* in the long-run," I reply in self-defense. "But maybe you're right, Kevin. Maybe I do need to back off on the command and control. I suppose that when it comes to people, control is nothing but an illusion anyway."

"Now that sounds like something a pretty smart person would

say, Dad," Kevin looks at me with respect.

I smile. "Yeah, a very wise person indeed."

CHAPTER 4

"You wanted to see me?" Melissa is standing in my doorway.

"Yeah, come on in. I want your opinion on something."
Melissa walks in and sits down cautiously.

"You want my opinion?" She acts as if it doesn't matter.
I'm not quite sure how to read Melissa. On the one hand, she knows her stuff. As our Human Resources Manager, she can recite nearly every labor law verbatim. She is intelligent, well-read, and she doesn't back down from anyone. On the other hand, she spends very little time outside of her office actually relating to our employees. And when it comes to the word "change," Melissa freezes up like an ice cube.

"Yes, I do," I continue. "I'm looking for ways to begin measuring the quality of our leadership."

Melissa now looks like someone who was just zapped by a jolt of electricity.

"What do you mean?" she questions.

"I want to know how our employees feel about the quality of service they're getting from our management staff."

"You mean like an attitude survey?"

"No. It's more than that. First, I want to do it on a regular, recurring basis - not every two or three years. And second, I want it to focus exclusively on leadership, not compensation and benefits and all that other jazz."

"Can I ask why you want to do this?" Melissa seems perplexed.

"To create a greater sense of focus and accountability. I want to know if the people around here are committed."

"What about our labor agreement?"

"That tells us we have agreement," I reply, reflecting on Jordan's words. "I'm interested in knowing if we have their commitment."

Judging by the puzzled look on Melissa's face, which probably mirrors the expression I modeled for Jordan, I proceed to explain the difference to Melissa.

"Well, I suppose if we're going to develop some kind of measurement tool, the first thing we have to do is define the criteria we're going to use."

"That's what I want your opinion on, Melissa. I want to know what you think it takes to lead people effectively."

"Wouldn't that differ from one person to the next?"

"I don't know. But I suspect that there are certain fundamental characteristics that apply to everyone. And I want to know what they are."

"So you want to know my definition of what it takes to be a quality leader?"

"That's right."

I watch as Melissa's eyes roll toward the ceiling. Either she considers this a waste of time, or she is searching for an intelligent answer.

"Well, the first thing I would say is that the person has to be credible and trustworthy. If I'm going to commit myself to a direction that someone else is setting for me, I have to believe they know what they are doing."

I scribble the words credible and trustworthy on a notepad.

"Otherwise, I might just go through the motions - what you call agreement. But my heart wouldn't be in it."

"What else do you think it takes to build a sense of commitment in people?"

"For me, it would be ownership. I am more likely to commit to something that I have a stake in."

"Like decisions?"

"Sure. I am far more likely to commit to decisions that I am involved in. Maybe that's one of those universal principles."

"I suspect you're right." I write down the words "involves people in decisions" and "gives people a sense of ownership."

"And I am far more likely to react favorably to someone who treats me with a sense of dignity and respect."

I add "treats people with dignity and respect" to my list.

"Anything else?"

"This exercise reminds me of a boss I had when I first got out of college," Melissa volunteers. Her eyes are still focusing on the ceiling. "I'll never forget the guy."

"What is it that made him so special?"

"Same things I just told you. He gave me a clear sense of direction and he treated me like a valuable member of the team."

I smile but say nothing, adding the words "clear sense of direction" to the list.

"And he wasn't afraid to take a risk. He was very action-oriented."

I jot down the word "proactive."

"There. How's that for a concise list?"

> * Credible
> * Trustworthy
> * Involves people in decisions
> * Gives people a sense of ownership
> * Treats people with dignity and respect
> * Clear sense of direction
> * Proactive

"Excellent," I reply, pulling a tattered index card from my shirt pocket. "Now take a look at the characteristics that Judy and I came up with."

I hand the index card to Melissa and she glances it over.

"Looks almost like we could all be describing the same person," she says without looking up.

"Yeah, but we're not."

"So maybe there are certain universal guiding principles that elicit quality leadership."

"I'm beginning to think there are."

"And you want to build these principles into our own management performance reviews?"

"That's right. *We get what we inspect, not what we expect.*"

"Won't Wayne love that!" Wayne is our Plant Manager, and one of the people Judy was referring to last night.

"So what do you think of the idea?"

"Well, it makes sense in theory. After all, we never really have defined our culture in explicit terms - let alone measure it. But what are you going to do when half the management team flunks?"

"Do you really think that will happen?"

"Let's just say I wouldn't be surprised." Melissa looks frustrated.

"Do you want to talk about it?" I pull.

"What good will that do, Jack? The fact is, I don't see how this will make much of a difference."

"Why? What's the problem?" I persist.

"Look, we both know that we've treated the majority of people around here for a long time like they don't have a brain in their head. When there's a problem, we say 'read the contract' or 'file a grievance.' When there's a crisis, we all start pointing fingers at each other. We're innundated with memos, proposal requests, constant changes, bickering, backstabbing. You name it." She pauses and takes a deep breath. "Now, you want to start measuring how lousy we are as leaders? People will slap that right back in our faces."

"Like you're doing to me right now?"

"Yeah, I suppose I am. But come on, Jack. Let's be realistic."

As Melissa says this, my first instinct is to fight back. After all, this is how I normally respond to attack. But instead, I say nothing. I just look at her. My mind drifts to Jordan. What would he do in this situation? What would he say to Melissa?

"Are you suggesting that we leave things the way they are?"

"No, but..." Melissa freezes. I can see her mind searching for a diplomatic reply. And without her saying another word, I discover the truth. The change has to begin with me.

"Are you looking for a polite way to tell me that I'm the first one who has to change?"

Melissa smiles nervously.

"You said it, Jack. I didn't." She pauses looking for a reaction. "It isn't that I'm not committed. It's just that I'm not really sure what I'm supposed to be committed to. And I'm tired of playing on a team where half the members are competing against one another."

"In other words, you want to win but you're not convinced we have a winning strategy."

"That's one way to put it," Melissa replies. "But that's assuming we have a strategy."

"What do you mean by that?"

"Well, I know we have a business plan and a mission statement and all that. But it seems to me that we don't have any kind of strategy aimed at pulling people together in a common direction. Most of our people wander around aimlessly like they're wearing blinders."

My mind drifts to Kevin. Melissa's words ring of truth.

"Go on."

"Everyone's just covering their own hides. They do what they know they have to do to get by. Nobody wants to rock the boat."

"No exceptions?"

"Of course there are exceptions," she admits. "But for the most part, our people are not committed from the heart."

"So do you think we can change that?"

It's obviously a two-sided question and Melissa knows it.

"To be honest, Jack, I don't think we have any choice. But you're going to have to back it up by making some pretty tough decisions."

We both know what she is talking about.

"And if I accept that challenge, will you accept mine?"

"And what is that?"

"That you commit to the principles of effective leadership."

"You have my word."

"And one more thing..."

"What's that?"

"Never stop challenging me when you think I'm wrong. I need to hear your point of view."

As Melissa leaves my office, I review her list of leadership characteristics knowing full well they do not describe me. I then glance at my own list and Judy's. Finally, I think of Kevin and the insightful comments he made about Ms. Marks. I laugh to myself. It all sounds so basic. How is it that so many people lose sight of this? How did I? And how am I ever going to turn things around?

CHAPTER 5

"Let's begin this morning's staff meeting with a little exercise, shall we?" I ask, circulating a pack of blank index cards around the large mahogany conference table.

Eyebrows shoot up suddenly as heads swivel my way. Melissa smiles. Most of our staff meetings drag on forever with long-winded reports that only interest the speaker. The idea of doing a participative exercise immediately gets people's attention.

"The first thing we're going to do is to write down our mission statement." I pause to let the words sink in. "Then we're going to write down what we think it takes to lead people effectively."

"What's this all about?" Wayne's eyebrows are still on top of his head.

"I'll explain after everyone has had a chance to jot down their answers."

"How specific do you want this to be?" asks Bill, our Contoller.

"I want you to be very specific," I reply.

Bill looks at me as if I'm slightly off my rocker. Wayne is still sucking on the end of his pen and looking around the room. His eyebrows have now reversed direction. Melissa is deep in thought. Finally, Roger, our Quality Assurance Manager, speaks up.

"Does this have anything to do with the audit we have next

week?"

"No. At this point, this has nothing to do with any external customer audits," I reply. "Although, I suppose it could in the future."

Roger looks back at the blank index card in front of him. Obviously, the three paragraph mission statement we have hanging out in the front lobby is not as clear to people as I had assumed.

The room becomes silent. Several minutes later, Melissa speaks up.

"Can I say something?"

"Sure," I reply. "Go ahead."

"Well, it seems to me that if we're going to expect our people to commit to a common purpose, we ought to at least know what it is."

"And what is it, Melissa?" Wayne attacks.

"That's just it, Wayne," Melissa responds boldly. "I don't think any one of us can recite our own mission statement. I know I can't. At least, not word for word."

"Let's cut right to the chase," I interject. "Can anyone in here tell me exactly what this company's mission is?"

The room becomes silent again. Eyeballs roll subtly from left to right.

"Okay, then can anyone in here tell me what it should be?"

"To get product out the door and into our customers hands," Wayne blurts out. "That's what pays our salaries."

"Quality product, that is," adds Roger. "If it isn't a quality product, then there's no sense in shipping it."

"What about innovation?" offers Jim, our Engineering Manager. "We won't be in business long if we aren't on the leading edge."

"To make money," suggests Bill. "The bottom line in any business is to make money."

"And how do we make money if we aren't treating our customers right?" adds Steve, our Sales Manager. "I think our mission is to take care of our customers."

"What about our own people," Melissa asks. "How can we take care of our external customers if we don't take care of our internal customers first?"

Wayne starts to laugh.

"Are you suggesting that we start treating the people on the front line like they're our customers?"

"That's exactly what I'm saying, Wayne. Maybe they ought to start evaluating our performance."

"You've got to be kidding," Wayne snorts, looking towards me. "All hell would break loose."

"And why is that?" I ask.

"What? You're siding with Melissa on this?" Wayne's eyebrows are back on top of his head again. "Come on, Jack, you know what it's like out on the floor. We have a job to do. If we start worrying about how the people feel about every decision we make, we'll never get anything done."

"Are you saying they can't make some of these decisions for themselves?" Wayne is starting to sound a lot like Kevin's basketball coach.

"I'm saying that if you want products shipped out the door on time, someone's got to make some tough decisions."

"And these decisions all have to be made by Management?" I probe. Wayne is unquestionably upset.

"What is this, Jack? Are you starting to side with the union?"

"Wayne, that's the second time you've accused me of siding with someone. First, it was Melissa. Now, it's the union. Has it ever occurred to you that we're all on the same team?"

A few people chuckle under their breath.

"So you agree that we should start having the people on the

line tell us what to do?" he mumbles, looking around the room for support. "I don't believe it!"

"Wayne, all I'm saying is that maybe it's time to start getting the people on the front line more involved in decisions."

"Why? Did we have a bad month or something?" Wayne refuses to consider the possibility. "Is that what this is all about?"

"On the contrary," Bill says. "November was a pretty decent month."

"Then I must be missing something," admits Wayne, shaking his balding head. "If we're making money and getting product out the door, why change things?"

"The problem is that we don't have a committed workforce," Melissa interjects. "Most of our people just punch in, go mindlessly about their business, and punch out at the end of the day. And our turnover stinks."

Like I said, Melissa won't back down from anyone.

"Face it, Melissa. That's reality! How can you expect people to get excited about a monotonous job like stamping parts or making boxes?"

"Let me ask you something, Wayne," I interrupt.

The man looks at me as if he's being betrayed.

Before saying anything, I think back to the discovery techniques Jordan used with me. *People are less likely to argue with their own data,* he assured me. Use this principle to overcome resistance. Ask insightful questions, and allow your audience to draw their own conclusions.

"What do you think our people on the front line really want?"

"You mean, why do they work here?"

"Yeah, why do they work here, Wayne?"

The man starts to laugh.

"As far as I'm concerned, all they give a damn about are their paychecks and benefit plans."

His assumption is not unique. I think of Maslow.

"You don't think they want more than that?"

"I know I do."

"And what is it that you want?"

Wayne hesitates and looks around the room.

"Well, to be perfectly honest, I want power. I want to feel like I'm in control of things."

No one in the room is surprised.

"In other words, you don't want some bureaucrat telling you what to do."

He pauses for a moment, as if pondering a trick question.

"That's right. And I want to be involved in what's going on. Nothing ticks me off more than being kept in the dark."

"Anything else?"

"Yeah, I want to feel like I'm doing something important - not wasting my time on some bullshit, flavor-of-the-month activity trap."

"Alright, I hear you." The man's choice of words are not always the most eloquent, but you never have to wonder what Wayne's thinking. "And as we both know, you want to be rewarded for your efforts."

"Naturally," he smirks. With Wayne, it's never enough.

I pause and look around the room. Everyone is watching me intently, wondering what I'm getting at.

"So tell me, Wayne. Is this so different than what the people out on the production floor want?"

"How the hell am I supposed to know? You're not paying me to be a psychologist."

"You're right. But I am paying you to inspire the people out in production to pull together as a team and reach certain goals. And I can't imagine you can do that without knowing what motivates them."

No one says a word.

"Let me ask you another question, Wayne." I pause to get everyone's attention. "Don't you suppose the people on the front line want to feel some sense of power and control over what they're doing?"

He does not respond.

"What about being kept well-informed and involved in decisions?"

Still no response.

"And how about feeling like they are doing something important - like their existence actually matters around here?"

"What are you trying to say? That they're no different than I am?"

"Of course, they're different, Wayne. And that's what we want. But we all have certain fundamental needs. And all I'm saying is that perhaps it's time we started looking for ways to identify and meet those needs."

"I second that," Melissa interjects without looking at Wayne. "What's worked for us in the past sure doesn't give us any guarantees in the future. As far as I'm concerned, we don't stand a chance if we don't start pulling together as a team."

"And we can't do that without a clear sense of purpose." I turn to the group at large. "So what is it that we want people to feel when they hear the name TYPCO?"

"If you ask me, we've convinced ourselves that we exist solely to make money and reward ourselves - despite our mission statement." The heads all turn toward Mark, our Purchasing Manager. "At least, that's how it looks from my vantage point."

"And what's wrong with that?" Bill quips.

"I think it's short-sighted," Mark replies. "I think it's a trap."

"Why is that?" I ask.

"To begin with, I don't think the people on the front line buy into it. I don't think it has any real impact on them. After all, they make a fixed amount of money despite our bottom line performance."

"Are you suggesting we cut them in on our bonus program?" Wayne asks.

"It would certainly get them focusing more on the bottom line," Mark replies. "But that's another issue. All I'm saying is that I think it's important to look at the big picture when writing a mission statement."

"What's that supposed to mean?" Bill asks.

"It means that we have to look beyond making money to other relevent factors."

"Like what?" several people chime in.

"Like getting customers to rave about us as a supplier. Like getting people to quit their jobs at other companies to join our firm because of the incredible opportunity we offer here. Like investing in long-term ideas that focus on growth and advancement, as opposed to short-term quick fixes. And like coming up with a mission statement that people can at least remember." The man pauses. "Do you want me to go on?"

"So you're suggesting that our mission statement should cover all of these factors?" Bill asks. "Don't you think it's long enough as it is?"

"I'm not suggesting we write a long mission statement. In fact, I don't think it has to be any more than a sentence. But that doesn't mean it can't cover everything."

"I'm afraid I don't follow you," Bill admits, shaking his head. "Doesn't it make more sense to get everyone focusing on the bottom line?"

"Think about it this way. Every company knows it has to make money in order to survive. But how many companies have gone from making big money to near bankruptcy because they lost sight of some of the other critical factors needed for long-term survival." Mark appears genuinely concerned. My guess is that this has been frustrating him for a long time. And here I am thinking he isn't a team player just because he normally keeps to himself. I think of my conversation with Kevin. Maybe Mark is one of those players who is committed to winning but doesn't think we have a winning strategy.

"Actually, I can think of dozens of companies in deep trouble," adds Nancy, our Customer Service Manager. "In fact, if we don't do something soon, we may lose one of our biggest customers."

"Which one is that?" Steve asks.

"Peak Performance," Nancy replies. "They're getting tired of our excuses on late shipments and inaccurate piece counts."

"I didn't know that," shouts Steve, as if awakening from the dead. "When were you going to tell me that?"

"I just found out about it last night," replies Nancy, covering her butt. "I left a memo on your desk."

"Couldn't you have at least called me?" Steve demands. "You've got my cellular number. That's my biggest account!"

Somehow I sense that Steve is more concerned about his commission on the account than he is on the jobs we could lose. Even though Steve is our Sales Manager, he handles a few large accounts personally and his compensation is tied to the sales volume of those accounts.

"It was late in the day and I knew I would see you this morning," replies Nancy in self-defense. "I'm sorry."

Roger jumps in. "Maybe if you paid more attention to the service we provide your accounts, Steve, and not just the dollars, you could have helped us avoid this problem to begin with."

"Hey, I'm not responsible for delivering the goods," Steve counters. "I just sell them. You guys handle the rest. We all have a role to play. Isn't that what teamwork is all about?"

My mind drifts again to Kevin and his basketball team. 'We have guys more interested in competing with one another than with our opponents,' Kevin had said. 'All they do is think about themselves.'

"Alright." I announce. "We'll work this out later. Right now, I want to get back on track."

"You see," Mark cuts in. "This is exactly what I'm talking about. While we sit here and point fingers at one another, one of our biggest accounts is planning to take a hike."

"So what do you think our mission statement should be, Mark?" I ask.

"Well, like I said before, I think it should be short and to the point - like Disney's - which is 'to make people happy.'"

As Mark says this, I remember Jordan saying the same thing in his workshop. 'Write your mission statement for the people on the front line, not the MBA's in the offices. And try to keep it to 15 words or less.' "So do you have any suggestions?" I ask.

"Actually, I wrote down three," Mark says, looking to a notepad in front of him. "The first one is 'to improve everyday.' The second one is 'to dazzle our customers.' The third one is 'to get people to say we're awesome.'"

"Isn't that a little vague and idealistic?" Wayne laughs. "Hell, we're not even close to any one of them."

"Well, isn't that the point of a mission statement?" Mark rebuts. "It isn't supposed to describe what we are. It's supposed to define what we seek to accomplish. It's supposed to give us a sense of direction."

"Shouldn't the mission statement define how we plan to accomplish this though - like the one we have now?" Bill asks.

"On the contrary," Mark replies. "The mission statement simply needs to address *what* we seek to accomplish, not *how* we plan to get there. That's where corporate principles and strategic planning come in. If we try to cover both the "what" and the "how", we're going to be right back where we are now."

"I like all three of them," adds Roger. "They cut right to the bone. If we improve everyday and work toward dazzling our customers rather than just satisfying them, we should be in business for a long time. Think about it. If our customers are telling people how great we are, we'll have all the business we can handle. Your mission statements sure cover the quality element, Mark."

"And the engineering element," adds Jim. "We won't dazzle many people if we aren't on the leading edge in product and process design."

"They cover the human element as well," adds Melissa. "That is assuming, of course, that we aim it internally as well as externally."

"We're back to that again, huh?" Wayne mumbles.

"Lighten up, Wayne!" Melissa fires back. "Are you that much better than everyone else?"

Maybe it's just the way Melissa says it, but suddenly I have a pretty clear picture of some of the tough decisions I have to make to turn my vision of a high performance work environment into reality. Even people like Wayne, with whom I've worked with for many years, will no longer be able to hide. Jordan made it very clear that change of this magnitude doesn't come without pain.

"Let's just say I've been around a while," Wayne returns. "You give an inch, these people take a mile."

"Alright, let's get back on track," I command for the second time. "Perhaps we can take the three suggestions Mark has given us and come up with one mission statement that we all agree on."

"How about 'to get our customers to say we're awesome and getting even better,' volunteers Roger. "Doesn't that say it all?"

"That sounds good to me," Nancy says. "It certainly gives us something significant to focus on in Customer Service."

"How about simply 'to get people to rave about us?'" suggests Melissa. "People won't rave about us if we aren't doing outstanding work. And by using the word people rather than customer, we cover employees, Corporate, shareholders, vendors, customers, the community - all of our stakeholders."

"I like that one even better," Roger says. "It's shorter, and it covers more ground."

"I do, too," Nancy adds. "That one's got my vote."

"I can live with that," Bill says. "It certainly implies that we aim to make money. People aren't going to rave about us if we're in Chapter 11."

"Do you actually think people are going to know what the word *rave* means?" Wayne asks pessimistically.

"If they don't, we'll teach them," Melissa replies. "Show a little faith, Wayne."

"Alright, do we have any other proposals?" I ask.

The room becomes quiet.

"Then let me ask if anyone has a problem with Melissa's suggestion, 'to get people to rave about us?'"

"I still think this is a waste of time," Wayne says. "How am I supposed to explain this to the people out on the floor?"

Suddenly, I remember a quote Jordan used in his workshop. It was a quote from Emerson: *What you are speaks so loudly, I cannot hear what you are saying.*

"May I suggest that you don't try to explain it, Wayne. You just start living it."

"What do you mean by that?"

"Let me put it this way," I continue, looking around the room. "What we are will always speak louder than what we say we are. Think about it. The only way to make this work is to demonstrate it, not talk about it. Figure out what it's going to take to get people to start raving about this place and just do it."

"Hell, I can give away the farm and people will rave about it," Wayne says under his breath.

"And be rational about it," I add. "People won't be raving about a business that's gone broke."

"I can come up with a whole list of things that we can start doing to get people to rave about us," Nancy offers. "But it's going to mean a lot of things have to change."

"Well, before we get into that, let's nail down this mission statement," I suggest. "Can you all live with the statement 'to get people to rave about us?'"

It's nearly unanimous. Wayne and Steve are the only two people holding out.

"And how many prefer the original statement 'to get customers to say we're awesome and getting even better?'"

No one's hand goes up.

"How about you guys?" I ask. I look from Steve to Wayne. "What do you propose?"

"Whatever you want, Jack," Wayne mumbles.

"I guess I can live with the raving statement," adds Steve. "I'm already doing it anyway."

There he goes again, thinking only of number one. How does the man live with himself? For that matter, how does anyone live with him? Then I remember the nasty divorce he went through a couple of years ago, leaving his wife and kids in the dust. Come to think of it, I think he's separated again now. Maybe I should spend a little time talking with some of the sales reps. I'm sure they can give me some useful insight on the quality of Steve's leadership. I just hope they don't feel like Kevin does about his coach.

As for Wayne, I probably ought to do the same thing. Somehow, over the years, I've lost sight of what's going on out on the factory floor. I just haven't made the time to get out there and talk to people - or listen to them. Seems I have the same problem with Kevin's basketball games and Kathleen's concerts. Maybe it isn't so much an issue of time but one of priority. I remember Jordan saying *"Time is only an excuse for people who haven't yet defined their priorities."*

"Okay. So we have a tentative new mission statement," I conclude. "Since Wayne is the only one here who seems to have a problem with it, we'll give Wayne until Thursday to come up with something better that we all agree on." Wayne's eyebrows spring up. "And if anyone else comes up with something better, I hope they will share it."

"So you want me to come up with something better by Thursday?" Wayne's eyebrows begin their descent.

"That's up to you, Wayne," I reply. "One way or another, we're going to move on this. I don't plan to take six months like we did the first time to come up with a decent mission statement. So if you don't have something better by Thursday, this one goes into effect."

The room is silent.

"And there's one more thing. I want all of you to finish part two of our opening exercise by Thursday. If we're going to start measuring the quality of our leadership around here, we better begin by defining exactly what it is we're going to measure."

"Measure the quality of our leadership?" Steve asks. "What are you talking about?"

"I'm talking about setting up a system that gives us feedback on the quality of our leadership."

"Can I ask why this is suddenly so important?" Bill asks. "Our numbers look fine. Doesn't that tell you something about our leadership?"

"Our numbers look fine in relation to what - what has been, or what could be?" I pause to let the question sink in. "Besides, when it comes to leading our people, I don't want to assume anything."

Judging by the anxious and suspect expressions glaring my way, I decide to invest the time in explaining my rationale. Twenty minutes later, our dry erase board is crammed with notes and diagrams ranging from Maslow to Herzberg to Deming to Jordan McKay.

"This sounds completely backwards to me," Wayne announces. "It's like you're changing the rules in the middle of the game."

"I like the idea," Nancy counters. "I think it's about time we started listening to the people on the front line and involving them in decisions. Not only will it help us become better bosses, but it will probably help us win another chance with Peak Performance."

"Why do you say that?" Steve asks.

"Because they're always complaining about late shipments, inaccurate piececounts, mixed colors, incomplete labels, inaccurate invoices, all kinds of errors that are made on the front line."

"So you're saying it's our fault?" Wayne interjects defensively.

"We're the ones who send out the invoices, Wayne," Bill offers in Nancy's defense. "The front line applies to us, too."

"That's exactly why we have to start paying more attention to our producers," I add. "They can probably give us hundreds of ideas on how to improve."

Suddenly the thought of getting three ideas per month through our suggestion box is embarrasing - and probably a slap in the face to a lot of our people. I wonder how many other well-intentioned programs we have that are perceived negatively. *"Message received is the only message that matters,"* Jordan said in his workshop. *"It's the people's perception that determines their commitment."*

"Well, like I said earlier," Nancy repeats. "I can come up with a whole list of things that we can start doing to get people to start raving about us."

"So can I," adds Wayne sarcastically.

"How about if we do this?" I suggest. "Take the next couple of days to identify what you would consider to be the top six or eight guiding principles that we must commit to in order to get people to rave about us - internally and externally. From here, we will begin to identify specific actions we can take to reinforce these principles."

"What do you mean by actions?" Roger asks.

"I mean changes that we have to make to reinforce the principles we say we believe in - things we can do to *'walk our talk'*."

"What kind of changes?" Steve asks suspectingly.

"I don't know exactly," I reply. "Once we define our principles, we will use them to cross-reference the systems and people we have in place to determine what needs to change. We'll take this one step at a time."

"So we're talking about people changes as well as systems changes?" Wayne asks. "I wonder how the union is going to feel about that?"

"The people changes will start with the people in this room," I continue. "We are the ones responsible for creating the company culture."

The room once again becomes silent. I realize that what I have just said probably comes off as a threat. But if I'm going to bring about any real change in this organization, maybe that's what a few people need to hear.

"Like I said earlier," Wayne repeats. "You're changing the rules in the middle of the game."

I pause and look at him. All eyes are on me.

"Wayne, do you really consider this a game?"

"It is to some people," he grumbles.

"Is it a game to you?"

"Yeah, it's like a game," he admits. "You have competition. You have teams. You have goals. You have rules. And you have winners and losers."

Again, Wayne's assessment is not unusual. In fact, I've used the same analogy many times myself.

"And what role do you play?" I ask.

"I suppose I'm an assistant coach."

"Okay. And as an assistant coach, what are you responsible for?"

"Winning," he says with a distrusting smirk.

"At what cost?"

"What do you mean by that?" His smirk tightens into a stern line stretched across his weathered face.

"I mean at what cost to the players and the rest of the coaching staff?"

"Hey, we all know that winning requires sacrifice," he says. "People have to put their personal interests aside if they want to win."

"And do you think the people working for you look at their life here as a game?"

"I don't know," Wayne replies. "Probably not. If they did, they'd probably be more eager to win. No matter what I tell them, they just don't seem to care. It's like Melissa said earlier, they just punch in, go mindlessly about their work, and punch out."

"So as coaches, we are failing?" I ask.

"I wouldn't say we're the best team in the league," Wayne replies. "But I wouldn't say we're failing either. We are making money."

"And what if we lose Peak Performance, not to mention others?" I probe. "Then what?"

"I suppose we have to replace them."

"And what if we don't eliminate the reasons why these customers are leaving us?" I continue.

"Okay, I get your point. We can't afford to lose."

"Which means we can't afford to have people who view themselves as losers," I add solemnly, making eye contact with everyone in the room. "This is why I took the time earlier to define the difference between agreement and commitment. We have to inspire our people to care about what they are doing - no matter what role they play. We have to build some inner-strength in our producers and teach them to think like winners. It may be the only sustainable competitive advantage we have left."

"It makes sense to me," Nancy concurs.

"I would like to think it makes sense to everyone," I reply. "But I realize it represents a pretty significant change from the way we've been conditioned to think. This is why I plan to take it one step at a time."

"So what's the next step? To identify our guiding principles?" Melissa asks.

"That's right," I reply. "We have to define our culture."

"Let's go to it," Mark volunteers enthusiastically.

"How about if we get back together at 8:00am on Thursday to confirm our mission statement and put together a consensus list of guiding principles? Does anyone have a problem with that?"

"I'm out all day on Thursday," Steve blurts out. "I have to meet with Americorp first thing in the morning."

"How about Friday morning?" I ask. "Does anyone have a problem with Friday morning at 8:00am?"

"I have vendors coming in at nine and eleven," Mark says. "Should I try to reschedule?"

"No," I reply. "Let's plan to meet at six on Friday. That should give us plenty of time."

"Six a.m.?" Steve asks in astonishment. "Are you serious?"

"I've never been more serious in my life," I reply. "Why? Do you have something more important going on at six on Friday?"

"Well, no, I suppose not," Steve replies. "I'll be there."

"Okay, so we'll meet at 6:00am on Friday. Everyone will come prepared to define our guiding principles. And, Wayne, you will come with alternative suggestions for our mission statement." I stop and stand up. "By the way, when you come in on Friday, I want you to come in through the plant. I trust it's been a long time since you've said hello to anyone on our night shift."

PART II

Define Your Character

CHAPTER 6

"So you rewrote your mission statement in one meeting?" Jordan's long distance voice rings with enthusiasm. "I'm impressed."

"Well, the truth is, I wasn't going to let anyone leave the room until we had something down on paper. The last time we tried writing a mission statement, it took us six months - and we never did compose any guiding principles."

"That's not unusual," the man says into the phone. "But, unfortunately, a company without a constancy of purpose is a company without roots."

As Jordan says this, I reflect back on his passion for this point in the workshop. High performance teamwork requires a solid foundation. Clearly defined principles give the team roots. They provide stability.

"And without these roots?" I lead him on.

"You know the answer, Jack. What happens to a building that has a weak foundation?" I can feel him smile.

"So it's an organization's principles that hold it together."

"They do more than that. They also set people free."

"What do you mean by that?"

"Principles also liberate and empower people to take risks and initiate action without fear of reprimand."

"How so?"

"As long as people feel that what they're doing is the right thing, they have no reason to be afraid. Principles advise you on what's right."

"Isn't that a little vague and idealistic in today's world? I mean, I could think I'm doing the right thing and still end up getting fired."

"What's wrong with that?" The man is perfectly serious.

I start to laugh. Suddenly, it dawns on me that the greatest leaders I've ever known, or read about, have gotten canned at least once. Either that or they've quit. They have a passion for doing what they feel is right, despite the adversity that comes along with it. It's like Jordan said. They're stable and consistent, yet fearless and free at the same time.

"I don't know. I guess maybe I've been conditioned to play it safe."

"You and five million other bosses, Jack. That's exactly why most people - and most organizations - never reach their potential. They hold *themselves* back."

"So you're saying that we have to use our principles as the foundation for building a high performance work environment?"

"That's exactly what I'm saying. And don't let people talk you out of it."

"Can you elaborate?"

"Sure. Let me begin by asking you how you feel about the word *integrity?*"

As Jordan says this, I begin to reflect on the relatively few people in my life who I would classify as having genuine integrity. Even my church has been in the newspapers lately for unethical behavior.

"Do you want my personal definition?" I ask, shifting the phone from one ear to the other.

"We can start with that."

"Alright. I would say a person with integrity is someone who you can count on to do the right thing. It's a person who is morally sound and complete - someone you can trust."

"Okay. Now, would you agree that integrity is an important element in high performance leadership?"

"Absolutely. Otherwise, your credibility is shot. People will question your motives. It's like that 'best boss' exercise we did."

"There you go. So how do you get people to believe you have integrity?"

Jordan hits the nail right on the head. The only way to convince people you have integrity is by demonstrating it. You have to "walk your talk". And you can't do that if you don't define the talk.

"I suppose it all starts when you give people your word."

"And in a world of continuous change, how can you say with any certainty what it is you're going to do?"

"I think that's where we've gotten off track," I admit. "There are always unexpected things popping up. That's probably why so many people at TYPCO don't feel we have any integrity. We change our minds every day."

"Do you change your mind about being honest?"

"No."

"Do you change your mind about being committed to on-going improvement?"

"No." I start to laugh. "But we do have a few people convinced that if it ain't broke, there's no reason to mess with it."

"How about working together as a team? Do you change your mind about that?"

"No. Although, some people stretch the definition of teamwork to fit their own agendas."

My reply is followed by a long silence.

"Listen to what you have just said, Jack. In a world of

continuous change, you have just defined three constants."

I stop and think about what Jordan has said.

"And I suppose there are more?"

"I believe there are," he replies. "But you must define these principles for yourselves."

"And without principles?" I probe.

"People make up their own rules. And generally, they're not consistent with one another because they're based on personal values, not on principles."

That's exactly the problem we have now. People are going in all different directions because their actions are driven by their own personal values, not by our guiding principles. There isn't anything holding us together. We're trying to build a skyscraper without a foundation.

"Remember this, Jack. Your mission statement alone is not enough to guide you in creating a high performance work environment. You need a set of fundamental *truths,* or principles, to lead you consistently in the right direction. This sets the foundation for establishing organizational integrity. It gives you the roots that ultimately determine your culture."

"In other words, organizational integrity means being in harmony with an established set of principles. It means valuing the principles."

"That's right," Jordan confirms. "Think of them like your lighthouse at sea. While the winds and tides will try to move you in different directions, you have a constant. You have a focal point. You have something to guide you in the right direction."

"And even though others may not initially see it, you still know where you're going," I add.

"Exactly," the man confirms. "But remember, it's the people's perception that determines their commitment. They must believe that you know what you're doing - even when they can't see your vision. Your people must discover for themselves that you're in harmony with these principles. What you are will always speak louder than what you say you are."

"Emerson," I whisper into the phone.

"You have a good memory, Jack. Use it to remember your guiding principles."

Once again, a light goes on in my head. This is Jordan's source of power. The reason he always seems to know what to say is because the words that come out of his mouth reflect the principles he has internally committed himself to. There is no guardian angel whispering into his ear. It's his principles that guide his behavior. He's like me - an ordinary man.

"Well, it seems we're on the right track then," I announce. "We plan to define our principles on Friday."

"Excellent. I'm always moved by people who actually do something with the information I share in my workshops. Many managers assume falsely that they're already doing it. That's why I prefer to talk first with the producers on the front line. They can tell you if the principles are being practiced."

"Well, I have to admit, you got my attention."

"In my business, you cannot be effective if you fail to get people to pay attention."

"I suppose that's true in my case, too."

"It's true in any situation where you wish to influence people without relying authority."

"I guess that means it applies to people everywhere." My mind begins to wander to the multitudes of people who could benefit from this advice.

"Think of it this way," Jordan says. "People who use only authority to get things done haven't yet discovered the power of using attraction. It's another factor that distinguishes great leaders from everyone else."

My mind leaps to Wayne, the ultimate authoritarian.

"Can I ask you something?"

"Shoot."

"Do you think running a company is like playing a game?"

"Not at all," he replies. "This is another dangerous assumption."

"What about the fact that there is competition, and teams, and goals, and winners and losers?"

"Sports analogies are one thing, Jack. But running a company is not a game." The man pauses. "First of all, people choose to play games. And when they make this choice, they realize up front that the game will come to an end and there will be winners and losers. And, more than likely, they can look forward to a rematch. This is what makes games challenging and fun. That is, assuming you like competition."

"I love competition."

"So do I," Jordan admits. "But not all people are alike. Most people work because they have to make a living. Work is a critical aspect of their life - not a game. They depend on it. And they don't want to lose."

"Sounds like something my son said."

"What's that?"

"That no one wants to lose."

"Makes sense, doesn't it?"

"Sure it does. So you're saying that it's dangerous to think of running a company or managing a department like playing a game?"

"That's exactly what I'm saying - especially, a department."

"Why is that?"

"Because people get confused about where the true competition lies. They end up competing with one another, rather than against the obstacles preventing them from mutual gain."

My mind leaps to Kevin's basketball team and then to my own management team. We're doing exactly what Jordan is saying.

"Why do you suppose that happens?"

"Because most people in our society haven't been conditioned to be team-players. In fact, they've been conditioned to be just the opposite."

"What do you mean?"

"Think about it, Jack. Do most parents teach their children consensus decision-making or autocratic decision-making?"

"Probably autocratic," I answer, reflecting on my own command and control style. "The parents make the decisions and the kids are expected to follow them."

"And how about the typical school system? Do you think it focuses more on independent learning or interdependent learning?"

"I would say independent."

"Now, consider your own work environment? Do your management systems put more emphasis on cross-functional processes, or independent tasks?"

"We still operate under the 'division of labor' mind-set. I suppose this means we set ourselves up for internal competition."

"Don't feel bad," the man explains. "Most systems do just that. In trying to simplify tasks, most organizations have complicated the processes."

"You mean the relationships between tasks?"

"That's right. And its the processes that matter the most."

"Why is that?"

"Several reasons. First, try this. Imagine you're a quarterback - say, Joe Montana."

"Okay."

"Now, how effective are you going to be if your receivers don't know how to catch the football?"

"I see your point. One task is dependent upon another."

"That's right. Improving one task without considering the other does not improve the overall process."

"What's another reason?"

"When you shift your mind-set to focus on processes, you often discover tasks that are totally irrelevent. They're either redundant, or they've become obsolete. This gives you a great opportunity to streamline your operation and increase productivity. You find that you no longer have to do some of the things you used to think you had to do. It's a whole different paradigm."

"And by focusing only on tasks, you could actually end up improving a task that isn't even necessary." I start to laugh. "Boy, that's got to get the bureaucrats' attention."

"There's a reason I'm in Washington right now," the man says humbly.

"Wow! Won't some of my people love this? It adds a whole new twist to our Total Quality Management program."

"Be careful, Jack. This is not TQM."

"What do you mean? Isn't this part of on-going improvement?"

"Call it whatever you want. But understand the difference. TQM typically asks the question 'How can we do what we do better?' This approach asks the question 'Why do we do what we do at all?' There is a distinct difference."

"So this mind-set concentrates on pulling the tasks together and eliminating unnecessary work. It focuses on the big picture."

"That's right. Joe Montana can spend hours throwing a football at a target to improve his accuracy. But that won't matter if he doesn't have receivers who can run their patterns properly and catch the ball."

Again, Jordan turns the lights on. It's like having Steve out promising our customers flawless quality and service without even considering the other elements of the process. He's just launching the ball downfield. No wonder our TQM efforts have been falling short.

"I suppose this opens people's eyes up to the interdependent nature of the business, as well?" I am now thinking aloud.

"There you go. It cuts through the monotony of isolated functions and gives people a greater sense of purpose and accomplishment."

My mind returns to Wayne's comment about all the monotonous work we have in our plant. "That's just the way it is," he had argued. Jordan is right. We're limiting ourselves.

"So if one of our guiding principles is to commit to teamwork - or put the 'we' in front of the 'me', as you put it - then we have to rethink our operating systems and organizational structure to promote more cross-functional, interdependent thinking and accountability?"

"That would be my guess. However, at this point, I'm not familiar enough with your organization to suggest any specific actions. You will have to discover these on your own - or contract help. Just remember, since most people are conditioned to think and work independently, you have to recondition them to think and work interdependently. This means you have to create a work environment that holds people accountable for cross-functional teamwork. Don't make the mistake of sending people to superficial team-building seminars and pep talks without backing it up with action. It only frustrates them."

As Jordan says this, I begin to wonder how many dollars we have invested in training - only to frustrate our people. Here again is a classic example of a well-intentioned effort turned sour.

"Let me ask you something else, Jack. How do you define your competition?"

"Well, technically, it's Americo and 4X and US Common. They're our biggest competitors."

"So if I went out and asked some of your producers to define their competition, is this what they would tell me?"

"I don't honestly know what they would tell you," I admit. "Maybe I should ask them."

"That was going to be my next suggestion. You can't create a high performance work environment without defining your competition."

As Jordan says this, I realize he's right. Even though this is not a game, we still have competition. We still have forces against us.

"I think that's one of our problems. We act more like our competition is internal rather than external."

"Maybe it is."

"What do you mean by that?" The comment shocks me. "Are you saying we should promote internal competition?"

He pauses to slow things down.

"What I'm suggesting is that you consider looking at your competition in a different way. Try defining it in terms of your mission. You may discover that it's a lot closer to you than you think."

"I don't understand what you're saying."

"Think about it, Jack. I have to head back into a meeting."

"Wait, where can I find you next week?"

"I'll be back in my office on Monday. But I leave for San Francisco early on Tuesday. Perhaps, we can talk late Monday afternoon - say 4:00pm?

"That sounds good to me," I reply, scratching myself a note. "And thanks again for calling."

"You're welcome," he replies. "Oh, by the way, will you have a union rep at your Friday morning meeting?"

"I wasn't planning on it."

"Have you considered the consequences of not involving your

union leadership up front in something this important?"

"I suppose I'd be leaving a lot of room open for assumption," I admit.

"And for argument against your data," he adds. "Think about it. *Involvement breeds commitment.*"

"Thanks for the tip."

"Define your principles, Jack, and these actions will become habit."

As I hang up the phone, I begin to wonder. How often do my actions violate basic human principles? Am I really that inconsistent? How can I expect others to adhere to principles I haven't yet defined for myself? Have I honestly been living a life of integrity, or have I just convinced myself that I'm a great leader, despite what others think? Could I actually be perceived negatively by people who I am assuming respect me? Am I using authority to get things done rather than attraction? Am I liberating and empowering people to feel like winners, or am I just forcing people to play by my rules? Does anyone think of me as a "best boss"? Do I dare find out? And who is our real competition, anyway?

CHAPTER 7

"Hi, Dad," Kathleen shouts as I walk into the kitchen. "What are you doing home so early?"

Judy turns suddenly and looks at me as if something's terribly wrong.

"I came home early to see if anyone wants to go to a basketball game with me tonight."

"You mean Kevin's?" Kathleen asks.

"That's right," I reply, kissing her on the forehead.

Kathleen doesn't respond.

"I'd love to go with you," Judy volunteers. "Is this kind of like a date?"

"Sure," I reply, turning to Kathleen. "How about you, Sweetheart? Do you want to go on a date with us?"

Kathleen smiles awkwardly.

"Actually, I'm planning to go to the game with Amanda. Her mom said she would drive us - if that's okay with you?"

"Well, I should have known a date with you would require more advance notice."

"And what about me?" Judy teases with both hands on her hips.

"Well, isn't spontaneity supposed to be romantic?"

"Good answer." Judy rolls her eyes. "I married quite the diplomat."

"So, Kathleen," I ask. "What was the best part of your day?"

"Today's not over yet, Dad," she quips. "Ask me again after the game tonight."

"I should have known better," I admit, remembering that Kathleen idolizes her sophisticated, older brother.

"How about you, Dear?" Judy asks. "How was your day?"

"Well, I came to some new realizations."

"What does that mean, Dad?" Kathleen is watching me intently.

"It means that I'm learning, Sweetheart. It means that I'm discovering new opportunities to improve myself."

"Like what?" Kathleen asks.

"Like paying closer attention to you and to your brother and to your mother, to begin with," I respond. "And like letting other people at work do some of the things I always thought I had to do myself."

"Is that why you're going to Kevin's basketball game?"

"Yes," I reply. "That's why I'm going to Kevin's basketball game."

"Does this mean that you'll come to my next concert?"

"Absolutely. You tell me when your next concert is and I will be there."

Kathleen smiles and looks at her mother.

"Did you hear that, Mom? Dad's coming to my next concert."

"I'm impressed," Judy replies. "It sounds like your father has had an interesting day."

"Well, hopefully we'll all benefit from it," I explain. "You see, Kathleen, my job requires that I devote an incredible amount of time and thought to what I'm doing. A lot of people depend on me." I stop and sit down on a kitchen stool. "But somehow, I've overlooked something very important. Instead of teaching people to manage themselves, I've trained them to depend on me. I've become a victim of my own system."

"What does that mean?"

"It means that my job has taken control over me instead of me taking control over my job." I watch as my daughter's expression changes from curiosity to puzzlement. "In other words, I've let my job tell me what I can and can't do."

"Why did you do that?"

I begin to laugh. How is it that an eleven year-old can make an adult feel so stupid sometimes?

"I don't know, Kathleen. I guess I never realized that there's no end to managing people this way. It's like that mouse you have up in your room. You know, the one that runs on that wheel and never gets anywhere."

"It's not a mouse, Dad. It's a gerbil."

"Well, whatever it is, it's not very bright."

Kathleen smiles.

"So where did this realization come from," Judy interjects. "Or need I ask?"

"Well, I did talk to Jordan again today."

"Who's Jordan?" Kathleen asks.

"He's a man I met through my work, Sweetheart. He's helping me make things better."

"How's he doing that?"

"He's giving me some very wise advice."

The girl's eyes suggest that I elaborate.

"Like how to get people to focus their energy on the things that matter most," I continue.

"That sounds like common sense, Dad."

Judy smiles and looks at me. Like her mother, Kathleen's nobody's fool.

"Maybe it's common sense for an eleven year-old. But somehow it's not common practice for an adult."

"You mean you have people at work who spend their time doing things that don't really matter?"

"That's right, Sweetheart. We do."

"Why?" Kathleen's beginning to sound like Jordan.

"Because they think their tasks do matter," I reply. "And because they want to protect their jobs."

"So even if they know it's not important, they won't tell anyone so they don't get fired?"

"Yeah, that's about right."

Kathleen pauses.

"Well, I can understand that. We have people who do the same thing in the orchestra."

"What do you mean?" It's now my turn to ask the questions.

"Well, they just sort of go through the motions," she clarifies. "They don't really care."

"Does your teacher know this?"

"I don't know. I don't think so."

"So how do you know?"

"It's obvious to the players, Dad. We sit right next to one another."

Suddenly, I hear Jordan's voice. *Pay attention to the producers, Jack.*

"Well, why do these kids even play if they don't care?"

No sooner has the question left my mouth and I discover the truth. It's just like some of the people we have at TYPCO. They have no choice. They have to work. And we still confuse agreement with commitment.

"Mostly because their parents make them." Kathleen confirms my discovery. "A lot of them hate playing in the orchestra."

"So they play because they *have* to, not because they *want* to?"

"That's right, Dad. I'm sure glad you and Mom don't make

me play. That would ruin everything."

As Kathleen says this, my mind wanders back to TYPCO. I wonder how many people we have in the organization who don't give a damn? On top of that, I wonder how many people we have doing things that don't even matter. It's certainly becoming clear to me why we need to assess the quality of our leadership and rethink our systems.

"So, Kathleen, does your orchestra leader ever ask you how you feel about playing the violin?"

"Not really. But I think he knows I like it."

"How about the other kids? Do you think he ever asks them how they feel about it?"

"He might ask," she replies. "But I don't think he gets the truth."

"Why not?"

"Because some of the kids lie." Kathleen pulls no punches.

"Is that so they don't get into trouble with their parents?"

"That's right."

"So how do you think the conductor could learn the truth?"

"By paying closer attention," she replies, as if the answer is simple. "If he just took the time to get to know the kids a little better, he would learn the truth. If you ask me, it's pretty obvious."

"Why do you suppose he doesn't do this?"

"He's too busy doing other stuff. I don't think he has the time."

"Or maybe he doesn't consider it a priority?" I ask, thinking of my own blurred agenda.

"You're probably right. He sure lets a lot of stuff slide."

As Kathleen says this, I begin to wonder how many people over at TYPCO are assuming the same thing about me. It's obvious that I don't spend much time observing and listening to people.

"Well, it's been fun talking to you, Dad," Kathleen concludes.

"But, I have to go. Maybe I'll see you guys at the game."

"Don't act like a stranger," I say, giving my daughter a hug.

"I was going to say the same thing to you, Dad." With that, Kathleen grabs her jacket, kisses her mother on the cheek and prances out the side door like a wild deer.

"Well, that was an interesting conversation," Judy laughs, sliding a bowl of pretzels in front of me.

"Yeah, I suppose it was."

"It sounds like you're a little worried about the music being played at work?"

"That's one way to put it."

Judy walks over and sits down on a stool next to me.

"So, do you want to tell me about your conversation with Jordan?"

"It's just that he got me thinking again."

"And what's he got you focusing on now?"

"Fundamentals," I reply. "Basic fundamentals."

"As in what?" she pursues.

"As in principles." I reach over and grab a pretzel. "He has me thinking I should define a set of guiding principles for TYPCO."

"Why is that so important?"

"They give people a constancy of purpose," I reply, munching on a pretzel. "They give people something they can trust."

"Like values?"

"No, not values," I reply. "Values differ from one person to the next. Even criminals value something." I stop and grab another pretzel. "Principles are universal truths. You cannot argue them."

"You mean like honesty?" Judy is now munching on a pretzel.

"Exactly. Honesty is a fundamental truth. It leads to credibility and trust. Live by this principle and people learn to trust you." I pause and twirl a pretzel in my hand. "Of course, not everyone values this principle."

"I see." Judy reaches for another pretzel. "So what other principles does Jordan suggest you live by?"

"He doesn't suggest any," I reply. "He doesn't tell you how to live your life. He simply stimulates you to think about how you can perform more effectively."

"So by living by a defined set of principles, he is suggesting you will be more successful?"

"That's right."

"Why?"

"Because principles give you focus and influence and power. People are attracted to someone who they can trust to do the right thing."

"I suppose that applies to us as parents, as well as professionals." Judy smiles.

"That's exactly why I'm sharing this with you. I'm making the same mistakes at home that I'm making at work. I've never really stopped to define who it is I want to be - as a father or as a manager."

Judy gets up and walks gracefully over to the refrigerator.

"So what principles does Jordan live by?"

"I wish I knew," I reply, reflecting on the depth of Jordan's character. "The man obviously lives by a powerful set of principles."

"Why do you say that?" Judy is peering into the refrigerator.

"For one thing, he always acts like he's got some guiding force with him. He always seems to know just what to say and do."

"You mean he's consistent?"

"He's very consistent. It's like his principles have become habit."

"And you think this enables him to be successful?"

"Well, he certainly is successful. And he certainly has had a powerful impact on me."

"What makes you say he's been successful?" Judy now pours herself a glass of orange juice.

"First of all, the man is focused. He knows exactly what he wants and he's doing it. He's published I don't know how many books. He gets paid over ten thousand dollars per day for speaking engagements. He works all over the world. He lives out on the Cape. He sails his boat all over the Atlantic. He's in command of his own time. And he's having fun."

"How do you know he's having fun?"

"Because it shows. He's doing exactly what he wants to do."

"Sounds like he has a constancy of purpose" Judy suggests, offering me a glass of juice.

"That must be it," I reply. "I suppose if he didn't enjoy doing something, he wouldn't do it - at least not for long."

"You should ask him what his principles are," Judy suggests. "Maybe he'll share them with you."

I pause and visualize Jordan's Socratic leadership style.

"No. Knowing Jordan, he'll make me figure it out for myself."

CHAPTER 8

"**G**ood morning, everyone," I say, glancing around the great mahogany conference table. "How was your trip through the plant this morning?"

"I saw some pretty surprised faces," Roger offers.

"I'll second that," Melissa adds. "It'll be interesting to hear what the rumor-mill reveals later today. People probably figure we're going to sell the place."

"What's your guess, Rock?" I turn to Jim Rockwell, the chief steward of our local union. His nickname speaks the truth. The man looks like he was carved out of granite.

"I suppose Melissa's got it right," he nods. "Most people on the night shift don't even know who you people are."

"Well, that's one of the things we need to change around here," I say sternly. "If we're going to pull together as a team, we're going to have to get to know one another a lot better."

"So what's this meeting all about, anyway?" Rock probes.

"It's about defining our future. It's about answering questions like 'Who do we want to be?' and 'What do we need to change around here to accomplish this?'" I can sense a few heartbeats accelerating as I say this.

"I figured those questions would have been answered a long time ago," the big man replies.

"Well, it's time to look at them again, Rock. It seems we have a number of inconsistencies in this company, and it's high time we cleaned them up."

"What do you mean by inconsistencies?"

"Let me answer that by asking you a few questions, Rock," I reply. "First, would you agree that we have a tendency to do the same task a variety of different ways?"

"That's for darn sure," he laughs.

"And would you argue that this is to our advantage?"

Rock looks around the room like I'm asking some kind of trick question.

"Not in my book," he says boldly. "It causes all kinds of problems. It drives people nuts."

"And how about our management style? Do you find that we're consistent from one department to another?"

The big guy starts to laugh.

"There's no consistent management style here. I've been saying that for years."

"Would you agree, then, that we can improve things around here by building more consistency into our operation?"

"Makes sense to me." Rock looks cautiously around the room. "As long as we all play by the same rules."

"Well, that's what this meeting's all about. We're here to define what it's going to take to pull this organization together and get everyone moving in a consistent, common direction."

"And what do you want me to do?" Rock asks.

"I want you to tell us what you think," I reply. "It wouldn't be right trying to do this without your input."

"Sounds interesting," he nods. "I'll do what I can."

I had given Rock some insight on the meeting's purpose when I extended him the invitation. Nevertheless, I wanted everyone to start out hearing the same thing. Rock and I go back a long time. We generally get along, but we still have our differences. Maybe it's the roles we play.

Rock seemed impressed that we were looking for ways to behave in a more consistent manner. In terms of interest, we had a consensus. He was even more impressed that we'd bring him in on the front end with something like this. Jordan was right. I had nearly missed an opportunity to build some commitment.

"So, Wayne," I ask. "Where do we stand on our mission statement?"

"I'll go along with the one we have," Wayne says half-heartedly.

"And does anyone else have alternative suggestions?"

The room is silent.

"How about you, Rock?"

"I like the one you're proposing. It sure gives us something to work toward."

"Alright, then," I announce. "TYPCO'S new mission statement is *'to get people to rave about us.'"*

"So how are we going to communicate this?" Melissa asks.

"I was going to suggest that we wait until we've defined our principles. Then we can explore ways to effectively communicate both. Does that make sense to everyone?"

Everyone in the room, with the exception of Wayne, appears to be in agreement.

"Does that make sense to you, Wayne?"

"I still think people are going to see this as a joke," he mumbles.

"What about you, Rock? Do you think people will see this as a joke?"

"They will if they don't see any action to reinforce it," the big man confirms. "Talk is cheap."

"That's exactly my point," Wayne adds. "They've heard all this before. Now they'll be wondering what the next flavor-of-the-month will be."

"Who have they heard it from, Wayne?" I ask.

"You know what I'm talking about, Jack. We send people to all these seminars and training and nothing ever really changes."

"And you don't think anything will change this time?"

"I don't know, Jack. You know how people resist change."

Suddenly, I remember something Jordan had said to me when I volunteered the same assumption.

"Wayne, do you really believe that people resist change?"

The heads all swivel toward Wayne.

"Isn't that common knowledge?"

"How about the rest of you?" I glance around the room. "How many of you would say that most people resist change?"

Nearly every hand in the room goes up.

"Then how do you explain the last Presidential election in this country?" I pause to provoke a reaction.

No one says a word.

"Isn't it true that our President was elected to *change* things? Wasn't that the general theme of his campaign?"

"That's true," Mark laughs. "In fact, that's true of most campaigns. We generally elect leaders to change things."

"And why is that?"

"Because we're looking for improvements," Nancy jumps in. "People perceive change just like anything else. They're looking for value-added results. It isn't *change* they resist. It's *pain* they resist."

"That's right. People support actions they believe are for the better, and they resist actions they suspect are for the worse. Your role as a leader, then, is to convince people that the changes we seek to make here at TYPCO are for the better. It's the only way we can improve." I pause and look around the room. "We've all got to become agents of change."

"Well, I've come up with some ideas on principles," Nancy

offers.

"So have I," adds Mark.

As Nancy and Mark say this, I begin to see two different people emerge from my previous characterization of them. Prior to our change initiative, both of them could have been defined as "show-up and keep-your-mouth-shut" types. They offered nothing above and beyond what was expected. It was like they were afraid to say anything contrary to the status quo. As for motivation, I had assumed they were only staying with TYPCO until something better came along. Neither of them showed much initiative. In one word, I would have described them both as having "plateaued".

"Alright, then let's get started." I get up and walk over to a flipchart standing in the corner. "How about if we begin by simply getting the ideas down on paper? We can edit later."

Grabbing a marker, I scribble the words TYPCO PRINCIPLES across the top of the flipchart.

"Let's start with you, Nancy. Give me one from your list."

"Think like the customer. If we're going to get people to rave about us, I think it's high time we start looking at our performance from the customers' point of view. And that means internally, as well as externally."

"Excellent," I say, hugging the flipchart and scribbling frantically. "Who's got another?"

"How about working cooperatively as a team," adds Mark. "We're never going to get anywhere if we keep fighting internally. The only way to achieve synergistic results is through teamwork."

"Great! Give me another." It now looks like I'm waltzing with the flipchart.

"Share information with people," Melissa blurts out. "We can't work well as a team if people don't know what's going on."

"Okay, that's three," I say, adding it to our list. "How about another?"

"Commit to excellence and on-going improvement," Roger offers. "If we're going to get people to rave about us, we have to go the extra mile."

"That covers quality," I reply. "Thanks, Roger."

"How about honesty?" Nancy asks. "If we want people to trust us, don't we have to be honest?"

"Can't argue that," I say, writing it down. "Give me another?"

"How about being consistent?" Roger suggests. "Don't we have to be consistent to get people to rave about us?"

"What do you mean by consistent?" Steve asks.

"It's like Rock said earlier," Roger explains. "We're driving people nuts around here by doing the same task six different ways. Committing to a principle like consistency will surely help us improve accuracy, quality, training, morale,... all kinds of things."

"Not to mention, management style," I add. "We're going to have to be consistent in adhering to these principles. Let's put it down."

"Involve people in decisions," Melissa adds. "It's like you said the other day, involvement breeds commitment."

"Okay, employee involvement is principle number seven."

"Involving people in decisions will only work if we listen to them with an open mind," Mark adds. "How about listen with an open mind."

"Beautiful," I say, racing to keep up.

"What about treating people with some dignity?" Nancy asks. "Doesn't that tie in with what we were talking about the other day - building people's self-esteem and helping them reach their potential? That goes beyond ownership to empowerment."

"Excellent, Nancy! That's a great suggestion."

"How about tolerating honest mistakes and using them as learning opportunities," suggests Roger. "Can we have some kind of principle guiding us toward constructive development of our people?"

"Great idea, Roger," I add. "That ties in well with what Nancy was saying. That gives us ten."

"What about holding people accountable?" Melissa asks. "To be effective, don't we have to hold people accountable for their actions?"

"That's true. Making honest mistakes is one thing, but carelessness and abuse of these principles cannot be tolerated. We'll add accountability as number eleven. All of our people will be responsible and accountable for managing their behavior in line with these principles."

"And what if they don't?" Wayne speaks.

"You tell me," I reply. "What should we do with people who continue to violate our guiding principles?"

The room becomes silent. All eyes turn to me. There is a long pause. I follow Jordan's advice. I smile and start counting silently to twenty. As expected, someone other than me breaks the silence.

"I'd say we get rid of them," Rock blurts out.

All heads turn toward Rock. Most of the staff look stunned. This is the chief steward of our local union. He's supposed to fight us on letting people go. In fact, he's supposed to fight us on everything. He's not supposed to suggest getting rid of people.

"Excuse me?" Wayne asks. His eyebrows are now nesting on top of his head.

"Well, doesn't that make sense?" Rock continues. "If you have people who continue to violate company expectations after progressive disciplinary action, what are you supposed to do with them - hide them in the closet and make life miserable for the rest of us?"

If only I had a camera to record the expression on Wayne's face. Talk about a paradigm shift. This guy's bubble was clearly popped. Of course, I had explained to Rock prior to the meeting that any people changes we make will start with Management. Even though Rock and I have our differences, we both have a pretty consistent description for Wayne.

"I think you're absolutely right, Rock," I add, reflecting on an analogy Jordan had used in his workshop. "If we don't pull the weeds, how will we ever get our garden to grow?"

Jordan compared building a high performance enterprise to cultivating a perennial garden. Teamwork is a natural process. It only grows if certain requirements are met. The roots represent the principles. They serve to renew the growth process year after year. A weed is an obstacle. It is not necessarily bad - just a plant out of place. To be effective, the leader must remove any obstacles to the growth process.

"And how will you be consistent if you continue to look the other way," Rock adds. "It's like you said, Wayne. People are going to be looking for action and results."

"Let's write it down," I interject. "This gives us twelve guiding principles. Is there anything else we need to add?"

"That looks like a pretty complete list to me," Nancy replies, after a long silence. "It covers everything I had in mind."

"Me, too," Mark adds. "I think it says a lot."

"If you ask me, I'll bet most of the problems we have around here are caused by violating one of these principles," Melissa says. "Now all we have to do is get people to consistently 'walk the talk.'"

"At least this defines our 'talk'," Nancy adds. "That's got to be a step in the right direction."

"Well, let me ask this," I probe. "Are there any principles suggested here that we do not agree on?"

The room becomes quiet. It's like Jordan said. Principles are universal truths. They're hard to argue with.

Okay, then, assuming these are to become TYPCO's guiding

principles, what do you propose we do next?" I walk back to my chair and sit down.

"I think we need to come up with some action plans before we say anything to the people," Mark suggests. "Otherwise, it's like Wayne said. People will just laugh."

"I agree," adds Rock. "People will have to see some proof before they even begin to take this seriously."

"Well, maybe this gives us an opportunity to put together some teams?" I ask. "Perhaps each team can come up with a plan of action relating to one of our guiding principles."

"That sounds like a good idea to me," Nancy adds. "When can we get started?"

"I was going to suggest that we start right away," I reply. "How about if we begin by forming a few teams around the first four or five principles? Each team's purpose will be to come up with recommendations on actions we can take to reinforce the principle."

After gaining general approval from everyone in the room, including a very quiet Wayne and Steve, we begin forming the teams. Fifteen minutes later, we have four teams.

"Okay, Team Number One will concentrate on Principle #1: *Think like the customer.* Nancy and Steve will coordinate this team, giving us representation from Customer Service and Sales. Make sure you get people involved from Shipping, Scheduling and Production, as well. Team Number Two will focus on Principle #2: *Work cooperatively as a team.* This team will be led by Melissa, Rock and Wayne. Please make sure you get others involved, as well. Team Number Three will concentrate on Principle #3: *Keep people well-informed.* I will work with Melissa and Bill on this one. Team Number Four will address Principle #4: *Commit to excellence and on-going improvement.* Roger, Jim and Mark will coordinate this team's activity. Let's just try to tackle the first four principles before going any further. At least, this gives us a start."

"When do you want to meet next?" Melissa asks.

"How about if we meet on the 5th at 8:00am in the plant conference room? That gives us about two weeks to come up with something."

"The 5th is a Saturday," Bill says, looking at his daytimer.

"I know that." Once again, I purposely choose a time and place that is contrary to our status quo. I want people to start thinking change. "That means we'll be working right alongside our production personnel."

The Rock is the only one smiling.

CHAPTER 9

"**D**o you have a few minutes?" I ask, leaning my head into Wayne's office.

"Sure," he replies, spinning toward me. "What's up?"

"Let's take a walk."

Wayne hoists himself out of his giant chair and follows me into the plant. The look on his face confirms I have his attention.

"Can I ask what this is about?"

I stop walking and turn towards him. The hum of machinery makes it impossible for anyone to hear what I'm saying unless they're within about three feet of me.

"It's about your future here, Wayne," I state firmly. "I need to know how committed you are to turning my vision for this company into reality."

Wayne's face reddens as his blood pressure rises.

"That's just great, Jack. I've been loyal to this company for over twenty years. And, now, suddenly I'm on waivers?"

I start walking slowly.

"Look, Wayne. I know you've worked hard to do what you think is right. And I appreciate that. But..."

"So what's the problem, Jack?" he interrupts. "It's not like we're in trouble. Is Corporate putting pressure on you?"

"No," I reply. "The problem is that if we don't change the way we're doing things, we're going to get ourselves into deep trouble. And rather than wait around for Corporate to tell us what to do, I want to initiate these changes now. As far as I'm concerned, this division has the potential to become a benchmark for the entire corporation. But to do this, we either grow and adapt to the world around us, or we eventually go by the wayside."

This time Wayne stops walking. I turn and look at him.

"Are you saying I'm going by the wayside?" The man looks humbled.

"No, that's not what I'm saying, Wayne. Although, that's a choice I'm prepared to give the entire management team."

"So what do you want me to do?"

"I want you to join me in my attempt to turn this organization into a high performance enterprise." I stop and look around the huge complex. "I want you to help me rethink the way we do things around here. And I want you to inspire a winning attitude among our producers."

"You don't think I want to get the most out of our people?" he asks. "Hell, I'm on them all the time."

"That's not what I mean, Wayne," I start walking again. "When it comes to people, control is nothing but an illusion. You can't get people to commit to excellence by using a command and control style. The best you'll get is a temporary agreement to do what has to be done."

"So what's wrong with that?"

"For one thing, it isn't consistent with our new guiding principles," I explain. "Forcing people to do things doesn't get them committed to going beyond standard - or, better yet, raising the standards. It's just a quick fix. In the long run, it probably does more harm than good."

"You aren't going to let those principles go, are you?"

"No, I'm not. We've developed them for a reason. And I'm concerned that what you think is right isn't consistent with what the rest of the management team thinks is right. You've got one set of rules and guidelines and we've come up with another."

"It's like I said before. You're changing the rules in the middle of the game."

I stop and turn towards him.

"To begin with, Wayne, this is not a game. The people here don't view it as a game, and neither do I. This is life. And, in my opinion, the people here deserve a quality life." I stop and nod to a young man in overalls walking by. "The last thing I want our people thinking is that they're losers in some sort of game."

"Isn't that just dodging the truth, Jack?"

"On the contrary, Wayne. It's facing the truth. It's treating the situation in a principle-based manner."

"So what exactly are you saying? Are you telling me I have to change?"

"I can't tell you to change, Wayne. That's a decision you have to make for yourself. But, what I am telling you is that this is for real. It's not a game. Going forward, our service as leaders will be measured by the people on the line - not just the bottom line."

"So you've bought into what Melissa's been chirping about."

"No, Wayne. Melissa's bought into what I believe makes the most sense for this company. It's a choice she made for herself."

"And you're suggesting that I make the same choice?"

"No." I start walking again. "I'm only suggesting that you consider the facts and make your own choice. I'll support you either way."

"What does that mean?"

"It means that if you choose to join us in pursuit of our mission and guiding principles, and your choice is genuine, I'll give you whatever support I can to help you through the transition. If, on the other hand, you choose to operate under your own parameters, and ignore the principles that we intend to pursue as an organization, I'll support you in finding another place to work."

"In other words, it's 'my way or the highway'?"

I lean over and pick up a $3.00 part laying in the aisle.

"No, it's 'our way', Wayne, and I'm asking you to give it a chance." I drop the part in a nearby bin. "Is it so difficult for you to see the value in what we're trying to do?"

"What I see is a soft, touchy-feely approach to doing business," he states boldly, as if testing me. "And I think it's going to cost you."

"Does this mean you won't even give it a chance?"

The man sighs.

"You know, Jack. I've been here for over twenty years. In fact, sometimes I feel like I live here. And I realize I can be pretty damn stubborn sometimes." The sharpness in Wayne's voice begins to soften as he searches for the right thing to say. "But, hell, I'd be a fool to burn any bridges at my age. I'll work with you on this. But you're going to have to be patient with me."

"I'll be patient with you as long as I'm convinced you're committed to turning our vision into reality." I stop and face the man. "But understand one thing, Wayne."

"What's that?"

"It's your customers' opinion that matters to me most. And it will be their opinion that I use to determine your commitment."

CHAPTER 10

"Want to join me for a game of basketball?" I ask, tapping on my son's bedroom door. "It's pretty nice outside." Kevin sits up in bed and rubs his eyes.

"Right now?" The boy is obviously taken by surprise. I normally spend Saturday mornings at the office - and Saturday afternoons working around the house.

"What better time than the present. I'll meet you on the court in ten minutes."

Before the boy can reply, I'm half-way down the stairs. There's no doubt he'll be right behind me. Even at fifteen, Kevin knows he can give me a run for my money on the basketball court. In fact, if it weren't for my flagrant fouling, he could probably beat me.

"So what are you going to teach me today?" I ask as Kevin comes walking out of the house half-dressed.

"What do you mean?"

"Well, I think you have some pretty good insight on the subject of teamwork." I turn and launch the ball toward the hoop - hopelessly missing. "And I've got to build more teamwork into our culture over at TYPCO."

The boy looks at me as if he's just been betrayed. He knows my mind is not on basketball - or on what interests *him*. It's still on

TYPCO, whether I'm physically there or not.

"You know, Dad. I don't really even know what you do at TYPCO." Kevin sits down to lace up his shoes.

"What do you mean you don't know what I do?" The rim rattles obnoxiously as I bounce another shot off it.

"Well, I know you're the General Manager at TYPCO. And I know you work your butt off trying to get people to do their jobs. You go to work early. You come home late. You travel all over the place. You don't take many vacations. And you constantly complain about people slouching off."

Kevin is right. From his perspective, all he sees is a stressed out, serious old man who can't seem to get a grip on things. I should probably tape record myself at the dinner table sometime. I'll bet I don't sound like much fun to a fifteen year-old.

"You sure don't make it sound very appealing." I dribble the ball over to my son.

"Other than that, Dad, I don't really know what you do."

That's probably because I've never explained my job to my son. As far as he's concerned, I probably resemble his basketball coach - bossing people around and dictating that they work as a team.

"So what would you guess my role is at TYPCO?"

Kevin hops up and takes the ball from me.

"I suppose your job is to make sure that the people who work for TYPCO are successful." The boy drives to the basket for a lay-up.

"Why do you say that?"

"Because that's the only way TYPCO will be successful." Kevin grabs his own rebound and rolls in a reverse lay-up. "And you have to make sure TYPCO is successful, right?"

"That's one way to put it."

Kevin's simplicity makes me stop and think. What am I doing

- and what is our management team doing - to make sure that our people are successful? Do they have the information they need? Do they have the resources they need? Do they have the proper training? Do they know how one function affects another? Do they know the score?

"So I suppose your job is to make sure that everyone is moving in the right direction." Kevin tosses the ball to me. "Am I close?"

"I'd say you hit the nail right on the head. In fact, I probably should have had you write our management job descriptions ten years ago."

"Why do you say that?"

"Because we've been overlooking one of the most important elements in your description."

"Which element is that?"

"The human element."

Kevin stops dribbling the ball and looks at me.

"That sounds a little bit like our basketball team, Dad."

"I know that, Son. That's why I'm sharing this with you.

The boy looks amazed. Here I am admitting to him one of my own deficiencies as a leader. This is clearly a first. I've never admitted a mistake to my son in my life.

"So what are you going to do?"

"Well, we're going to start by paying more attention to the people on the front line. It's like you said, we can't succeed as a company if the people on the front line are set up to fail."

The boy looks at me like he's suddenly figured out the cause for my recent change in behavior. I'm actually paying more attention to him.

"So how about you, Kevin. What do you want to do for a living?"

"I don't know, Dad." He swats the ball from my hands and

takes it to the hoop. "Right now, I just want to pursue basketball."

"Why is that?"

"Because it's fun. It makes me feel a part of something. It gives me a sense of accomplishment."

"What else turns you on?" It's time for me to start learning about my son's dreams.

"You mean like girls and stuff?"

"Sure. Girls. School. Dreams."

"Well, I don't dream much about school." The boy launches a jump shot. "But I do dream about girls."

"Anyone in particular?"

"Are you sure this is more important than your work, Dad?"

I laugh.

"You bet it is, Kevin. And a lot more fun." I motion for the ball.

"Well, there is this one girl in my Science class who I kind of like." He tosses me a bounce pass.

"What's her name?" I swish a jumper and motion for another.

"Kate," the boy says sheepishly.

"And what's so special about Kate?"

"For one thing, she's gorgeous." Kevin goes after my missed hook shot.

"And beyond that?" I huff.

"She's just really cool, Dad. She isn't all caught up in herself like a lot of the other girls. She's just really decent."

"So, are you going to ask her to a dance or anything?"

"I thought we were going to talk about teamwork?" The boy is starting to work up a sweat from chasing the ball around the court. Either that, or he's nervous.

"Can't we qualify this as teamwork? I'd love to hear more about Kate."

"Maybe some other time, Dad. For now, let's just say that me and Kate are good friends. She just doesn't know it yet."

"So how did it feel to finally win a game this week?" I ask, spinning the basketball on one finger for all of about a second.

"It felt great. But our record's still lousy."

"Well, do you suppose maybe you're starting to turn things around?"

"No." The boy motions for a pass. "We just played an easy team."

"So the root causes to your problem are still there?"

"Couldn't you tell, Dad? You were there. We still don't play well as a team. People hog the ball. Some guys never play any defense. And the coach just sits there and doesn't do anything about it."

"What would you suggest he do?"

"Teach us to play as a team," he grunts, as he takes a shot.

"And what about the guys who refuse to put the team's interests first?"

"Don't play them." Kevin never takes long to answer. "It's not like we're winning to begin with."

The boy is right about that. His team is losing and certain guys are being rewarded for it by getting more playing time. There's no accountability for teamwork. Therefore, there's no synergy.

"So you think you have the same problem at work, Dad?"

"Actually, I think we have the same problem everywhere. It seems we've become a very self-centered society."

"What do you mean by that?"

"I mean, people all seem to be asking the same question - 'What's in it for me?'"

"It sure seems that way at school." Kevin throws me the ball. "Everybody's playing by a different set of rules — their own!"

"Well, that's what I have to change at TYPCO."

"How are you going to do that?"

"The first thing we have to do is establish a common set of rules. You see, it seems most of our problems revolve around the absence of certain principles. It's like your basketball team. If each of your players committed to a common set of principles, many of your problems would probably disappear."

"That makes sense to me."

"That doesn't mean you win every game," I continue. "But it helps you play more cohesively as a unit."

"What does that mean?"

"It means you stick together. And in the business world, sticking together is a significant advantage. It's very hard to copy."

"So how come people don't stick together at work?"

"I trust it's for the same reasons they don't play well together on your basketball team. They either haven't learned how to work together cooperatively, or they aren't being expected to."

"Or both," Kevin suggests.

My mind jumps to Wayne. Here is a long-term employee who has never learned to work cooperatively with others. He's never learned to put the "we" in front of the "me". Either that, or he's never been held accountable for doing so. Now he has to make a choice. I sense a storm is coming and I'm causing it.

"So how about a little one-on-one anyway?" I ask, snatching the ball away from Kevin. "You still think you can take your old man?"

"Let's find out," the boy replies. "Age before looks. You take out the ball."

PART III

Understand Your Competition

CHAPTER 11

"**L**earn by observation," Jordan suggests into the phone.

"So you won't just tell me what your guiding principles are?" I repeat, heeding to Judy's suggestion.

"You'll figure them out soon enough. Consider it a test of your perception skills."

"Well, when will my test be graded? I need answers."

"What you need, my friend, is truth. Confucius once said 'What I hear, I forget; what I see, I remember; what I do, I understand.' Do you know what this means?"

"Sure. It means that people learn best by discovery."

"That's right. Knowing the answers isn't enough. To lead people effectively, you must discover the truth within the answers." The man pauses. "Tell me something, Jack. Have you ever met anyone who can tell you all about a subject like leadership or teamwork, but then turns right around and does just the opposite?"

"Yeah, I can think of quite a few people."

"In other words, they know what they're supposed to do, but they don't actually do it."

"I see it all the time. In fact, I probably do it myself."

"This is why I prefer not to tell you what my personal mission and guiding principles are. If I did, you would only know the answers on the surface. You wouldn't necessarily understand the truth that lies beneath them - nor would you understand how to apply them."

"So by observing you in action, I learn not only what your constancy of purpose is, but I learn how to apply the principles, as well."

"That's correct. This is why sending people to training on subjects like leadership and teamwork so often fails. These are principle-based values. People learn them by observing them in action and witnessing the power that stems from them, not by hearing about them."

"In other words, people need a mentor to learn how to lead effectively?"

"It sure helps."

"Well, that certainly explains why we have so much inconsistency at TYPCO. We haven't supported our people with good mentors."

"Do your managers understand that they're expected to be good mentors?"

"Probably not. I'll bet some of them don't even know what the word means."

"And what does it mean?"

"A mentor is a wise and loyal advisor. It's someone who helps you grow and become more successful." I stop and reflect on Kevin's description of my job. It's what I should be doing more of myself.

"So, why do you suppose some of your managers don't consider this part of their job?"

"Probably, because we've never clearly expressed it."

"Or measured it?"

"That's for sure. We've never evaluated our performance as mentors."

"Perhaps it's time to start. Remember, you get what you

inspect,..."

"Not what you expect," I interrupt. "I know. I know."

"So, tell me more about your meeting on Friday," Jordan says. "It sounds like you came up with some very powerful principles."

"I believe we did. Twelve in all."

"The number is not important," he cautions. "A lot of people get hung up on numbers. Don't make this mistake."

"Well, there were some people who thought we should trim it down to five or six after the meeting," I admit. "They didn't think people would remember twelve principles."

"They won't remember five or six either, if the principles do nothing more than hang on your wall. Besides, this isn't a test. People don't have to memorize the principles to pass the course."

"That's reassuring."

"But they do have to work by them to remain at TYPCO."

"I suppose this is where things get a little hairy."

"You're right. Once you've defined your direction and explained it clearly to your people, you must begin the process of *alignment*. This is where the rubber meets the road. This is where people will be looking for some integrity."

"So by alignment, you mean getting everyone moving in the same direction."

"Just like the tires on your car. And it isn't just the people you have to align."

"What do you mean?"

"You must also align your systems. If you change your people without changing your systems, you'll just end up with more of the same. Remember this - most people simply conform to the systems they work with. It's like Aristotle said, 'We are what we repeatedly do.'"

I laugh to myself. Where does he come up with all these little sayings?

"What about people who think I've changed the rules in the middle of the game?" I ask. "What do you suggest I do about them?"

"We've already discussed the fact that this is not a game," Jordan answers. "I would begin by clarifying that." My mind races to Wayne. "Secondly, you must take ownership for the fact that you have people who are conditioned to behave otherwise - as non-team-players. After all, you created the systems they have to work with."

As Jordan says this, I realize he's right. Without systems that reinforce our principles, and without mentors to demonstrate them, we cannot possibly expect our people to move in a common, united direction. Most of our employees don't even know what direction it is we're trying to go. And since it's our management team that has created our existing systems and hired the people, we have to take ownership for turning things around. Pointing fingers at one another certainly isn't going to change anything.

"What about managers who don't buy into our principles?" I ask, thinking of Wayne and Steve. "What can I do about them?"

"Ultimately, they become obstacles to your advancement. They cost you integrity."

"That they do," I confirm.

"And didn't you just finish telling me that one of your guiding principles was to pull the weeds?"

"Yes, I did."

"And what did we conclude that integrity means?"

"It means being in harmony with your principles," I reply. "So that means I have to start pulling some weeds?"

"It means you have to begin the process of determining where the weeds are," he advises.

"How do I do that?"

"There are three important steps to the process," he explains.

"The first thing you have to do is to define your direction and your expectations. And this includes abiding by the organization's guiding principles. Every member of the company has to know exactly what is expected of them. Without this information, they are not equipped to win."

"In other words, if they don't know exactly what is expected, they could actually think they're doing a good job when, in fact, they're not?"

"Precisely," Jordan says. "Call it a "Perception Warp". It's when their perception of their behavior is different than your perception of the same behavior."

"So if I have a manager who thinks he's getting the most out of his people by climbing all over them, but in fact he's just creating more problems, then this would be an example of Perception Warp?"

"That's a good example," the man says. "And if you aren't careful, Perception Warp will destroy your own integrity and credibility."

"In other words, it will destroy our people's commitment," I reply, remembering Jordan's admonishment of this disease in his workshop.

"That's right. True leaders anticipate and destroy Perception Warp."

"How do they do that?" I ask.

"Think about it. You'll discover the answers soon enough."

"So you aren't going to tell me?"

"Not today," he answers. "You can tell me when you figure it out."

"Somehow, I knew you were going to say that."

"Then you're beginning to understand one of my principles." I can sense the man smiling.

"What about Step Two?" I ask. "You said Step One was to

make sure that everyone knows exactly what is expected of them. What is Step Two?"

"Step Two is to provide them with the guidance and support they need to be successful. This means your role becomes one of a mentor and a coach."

"So, for example, I have to teach my managers how to become good mentors themselves?"

"If you want a high performance work environment, you have no choice."

"What's the third step?"

"Measurement," the man says. "The system is not complete without accountability. The last step of the cycle, then, is to provide feedback. Every member of the organization has to know how they are doing in relation to what is expected."

"So this involves some kind of performance review?"

"Yes. But don't get hung up on performance reviews as most people know them," Jordan warns. "Most of these systems fail to accomplish what they should."

"What do you mean?"

"You tell me," the man rebuts. "What is the purpose of a performance review?"

"To provide feedback and create a sense of accountability."

"In relation to what?" he pulls.

"Goals and expectations."

"Whose expectations?"

"Whoever the person works for," I say.

"And who is that?"

I'm about to say the person's boss, but I catch myself. I see what Jordan's driving at. It isn't really the boss we work for. It's the customer - both internally and externally. It's the people we serve horizontally, not just vertically.

"I suppose that would be the customer," I reply, reflecting on one of our new guiding principles. "Both internally and externally."

"There you go. It's the customers' perception of your performance that matters most. It's like my workshops. Your opinion is the only one that really means anything. My opinion is irrelevent."

"I see what you mean. Most performance review systems focus on vertical feedback, not on horizontal feedback. We have bosses doing the reviews, not peers. Our whole system is probably backwards."

"That all depends on who you want your people to be accountable to. If you want your maintenance people to be accountable to the people they service, for example, build that into your performance management process. It's like having a repair person come to your house. You know what you expect, and you're in the best position to evaluate the work."

"Hmmm. That changes things quite a bit."

"Yes, it does. Remember something, Jack. Most companies have designed teamwork right out of their culture because they've based their systems on an entirely different set of assumptions. If you want to cultivate a high performance work environment, you've got to be prepared to rethink these assumptions and to reengineer your systems accordingly."

"I suppose you're right."

"One more question while we're on the subject of performance management. Do you think a performance review should be more for developmental purposes or judgemental purposes?"

"Hopefully, developmental purposes," I reply. "A high performance work environment requires on-going learning and development."

The man pauses.

"And is this how you would say most people perceive the

traditional performance review process?"

"On the contrary," I reply. "I suppose most people see the system as critical and judgemental. It's a matter of checking a bunch of boxes and filling out forms. Even the people giving them don't like doing it."

"In other words, the typical system defeats it's own purpose."

"Yeah, it probably does."

I think of TYPCO. First of all, our people don't really know what is expected of them - at least, not in relation to our guiding principles. How could they? We've never even defined these principles. Secondly, most of our people don't know what their customers expect from them because most of them don't think they even have a customer. They assume the customer is outside the company. And, as for the actual review, our system is cluttered with judgemental evaluation forms and irrelevent nonsense. The emphasis is clearly on what the boss thinks, or on what the Human Resources department thinks, not on what the customer thinks.

"So, you're suggesting that we develop measurements that hold our people more accountable to their customers?"

"Now you're beginning to understand what a high performance work environment is all about, Jack. It's radically different than what we've always taken for granted. It holds people accountable horizontally, as well as vertically."

"So systems like our performance review process are likely to change dramatically?" I ask, recognizing a change that's been needed for a long time.

"If you intend to 'walk your talk', let your principles tell you what to do. In time, you'll learn to trust them."

"Wow," I whisper into the phone. "I'm not sure a lot of our people are ready for this."

"Help them to see the value in it and they may surprise you."

"But what if they aren't committed?" I ask. "What do I do

then?"

"Begin with the people who have to lead the change," he says. "You cannot cultivate teamwork without developing a constituency of true leaders. Work through the three-step cycle we just discussed. First, define your expectations. This includes committing to your mission and guiding principles, any specific job-related objectives and measurements, and a timetable for conformity. Don't forget to establish a timetable. Otherwise, you won't get the sense of urgency and consistency you need to expedite the transition process."

"What do you consider a reasonable timetable?" I ask.

"That's a personal choice. If it were my integrity on the line, I wouldn't let it go beyond three or four months before I started pulling some weeds."

"In other words, I owe it to my managers to give them a few months to adjust to their new roles - once the new roles are clearly defined."

"It isn't what you owe your managers," Jordan explains. "It's what you owe your *people*. Think of your organization as one. Don't get all caught up in this who's who business. Concentrate on what is best for the unit as a whole."

"How will I know that?"

"Use your eyes and ears," the man replies. "Observe people. Pay attention to them. Listen with empathy and an open mind. Isn't that another one of your guiding principles?"

"Yes, it is."

My mind leaps to Kathleen and her orchestra. I remember asking her a similar question. "By listening and observing," she had replied. "If he just took the time to get to know the kids a little better, he would learn the truth. If you ask me, it's pretty obvious."

"You may even want to develop a simple assessment tool that measures your performance in relation to your principles," Jordan continues.

"This goes back to measuring the quality of our leadership, doesn't it?" I ask.

"That's right. It accomplishes three very important things. One, it makes your leadership team more accountable to the producers on the line. Two, it tells those leaders exactly what you're going to measure. And, three, it gives all of your people some evidence that you're committed to 'walking your talk.'"

"Won't that change some assumptions around the plant?" I mutter.

"I trust it will. Just remember something - What people hear, they forget; what they see, they remember; what they do, they understand."

"Confucius," I say.

"Don't ever forget it."

"Thanks. I won't."

"One other suggestion before I go," Jordan says.

"What's that?"

"Form your action teams around your systems and procedures, *not* around your principles. And don't overlook your true competition."

"What do you mean by that?"

"You tell me in two weeks. You'll figure it out."

This time when I hang up the phone, I don't know what to think. On the one hand, I'm proud of myself for the way I handled Wayne. I sense that I'm on the right track. I also feel like I'm beginning to understand the core source of Jordan's extraordinary power - the true meaning within the answers. On the other hand, I'm apparently doing something wrong with respect to the teams I've set up. What did he mean by advising me to form the teams around systems and procedures? What's wrong with forming them around our principles? What difference does it make? And why does he keep bringing up our true competition? What a pain in the ass!

CHAPTER 12

"**I** have another question for you, Kathleen," I announce as we begin to delve into our ice cream cones.

She looks at me with a puzzled expression on her face.

"What's with all the questions lately, Dad? Are you feeling okay?"

"I'm feeling great, Sweetheart," I reply, licking my lips. "I just want your opinion on something."

"I mean lately, Dad, you've been acting really strange," she continues. "Driving me to school, taking me to the movies, going to my concert, and now ice cream. It just seems really weird."

"Am I getting in your way?"

"No," she replies. "I'm just not used to having you around so much. Kevin thinks something's wrong."

"Like what?"

"I don't know. Like maybe you're sick or something."

"I'm not sick, Kathleen," I laugh. "At least, I don't think I am. I'm just trying to do a little more listening and observing. You and your brother are growing up fast. Sometimes, I feel like whole years have gone by that I can't account for."

"Whole years have gone by, Dad," she blurts out. "Do you know that this week's concert was the first concert you've been to all year?"

"What about the one in October?" I rebut.

"It doesn't count when you only come for the last ten minutes," she states boldly. I didn't realize she paid such close attention.

"Well, can I ask you my question or not?" I repeat.

Kathleen pauses and then takes a long, around-the-edge lick of her ice cream cone. Her strawberry-blond hair and hazel-green eyes mirror her mother's, but her temperament matches mine.

"Go ahead, Dad," she mutters. "What's your question?"

"My question is, who would you consider to be your competition in the orchestra?"

"What in the world kind of question is that?" she blurts out. "Why are you so interested in the orchestra all of a sudden?"

"Because I know you are," I reply with a smile.

"Well, first of all, you have to understand that the orchestra isn't like a game," she explains. "It's more like a journey. At least, that's how our teacher explains it."

"What does he mean by that?"

"Well, it never really ends," Kathleen continues. "He says there's always room for improvement. You can always learn something new."

"So, in other words, you don't really have any competition?" I ask.

"No," she replies, wiping her mouth with a napkin. "We have competition, but it's not what you would think."

"What do you mean?" I ask curiously.

"My competition in the orchestra is myself," she explains. "It's the only thing I really have any control over."

"You're right, Kathleen," I admit. "I never thought of it that way."

"You see, Dad," she continues. "Our goal as an orchestra is to make great music. My goal as a performer is to contribute to that. Anything I do to limit myself, or move us in the wrong direction, is considered competition."

"So a mistake would be considered one of your competitors?" I ask.

"Not if it helps me to learn and grow as a musician," she replies. "Remember, playing in the orchestra is more like a journey, not a game. A mistake is only considered an enemy if it's one I don't learn from."

"It sounds like you have a pretty interesting teacher," I reply, swirling my tongue around my cone.

"Yeah, he's okay."

"What about the fakers, though? Is he still in the dark about them?"

"I've been wondering the same thing ever since we talked about that," Kathleens replies. "And do you know what?"

"What?"

"He does know."

"How do you know that?"

"Because he told me." Kathleen's eyes radiate when she smiles.

"You mean you asked him?"

"Yeah, I couldn't help it," she explains. "It was really starting to bother me."

"So, what did he say?"

"He said it bothers him, too. But some parents insist on making their kids do what *they* want, not what the kid wants. And, as a teacher, he just does what he can to help them develop an appreciation for music. I kind of feel sorry for him."

"Why is that?" I ask.

"Because I would hate to have to try to teach someone who didn't want to learn - especially a subject like music where you have to commit your heart and soul."

"Is that what your teacher tells you it requires?"

Kathleen takes a crunch out of the side of her cone.

"Yeah, if you want to be any good at it."

"How do the other kids feel about that?" I wonder aloud.

"The kids who want to be great think it's great."

"And the others?"

"They don't really care. They think it's a big joke."

As Kathleen says this, I find myself back at TYPCO. Change a few names and add a few years and our people are no different. We have some who want to be great performers. And we have others who think it's a big joke. And we probably have a majority who fall somewhere in between, wondering whether their efforts make any difference at all.

"Does that bother you, Kathleen?"

"Yeah, it bothers a lot of the kids. It doesn't seem fair."

"So why don't you do something about it?"

"Like what, Dad?"

Kathleen's right. What is she supposed to do? She's eleven years-old. And she's captive in a system that tolerates non-committed performers. For that matter, the non-committed performers are captive, too. Judy's always talking about how depressing some of the parents are at the PTA meetings. Imagine not allowing your children to pursue their own dreams.

"Well, what about your teacher? Isn't there anything more he can do?"

"Nothing's going to change, Dad." Kathleen sighs. "That's just the way it is."

A pit forms in my stomach. My own daughter is expressing what hundreds of people at TYPCO probably feel. They're trapped in a system that smells of mediocrity.

"So what are you going to do?"

"I'm going to keep playing for as long as I like it. Maybe someday I'll be in an orchestra where everyone is committed to the same goal."

Or maybe you'll end up with a company like TYPCO, I think, where the culture beats your attitude into one of hopelessness.

"That sure would be nice, wouldn't it, Sweetheart?"

"At least, I would know my efforts were contributing to something important," she says. "Right now, I just get lost in the shuffle."

Looking back on Kathleen's recent concert, I suddenly feel sorry for my little girl. Despite words of encouragement, she and I both know her orchestra is not very good. In fact, I'm a little bit surprised that she sticks with it. Half the kids don't seem to know what's going on. The other half play their hearts out, but for what? The end result is clearly short of what most people would describe as pleasing to the ear. Rather than synergy, this group has somehow figured out a way to defy the power of teamwork. It's like Jordan said, a small hole can sink a big ship.

But, then, who am I to point fingers? We're doing the same thing at TYPCO. It isn't that we don't have talented people. It's just that we've buried them in a system that fails to stimulate high performance. Instead of leading the pack, we have people with heart and soul wondering if their efforts make any difference - perhaps even waiting for a better team to come along. And what about our competition? Could it be right in front of us like Jordan said?

"Promise me one thing, Sweetheart," I hear myself say. "Never give up on your dreams. If your vision is to make great music, don't let anyone stop you. Someday your music may change the world."

She smiles at me innocently and then proceeds to take another giant crunch out of the side of her cone. I wonder if this little girl has any idea how much I truly care about her.

CHAPTER 13

"Good morning." I stand as Melissa and Bill walk into my office.

"Good morning, Jack," they echo.

I motion for Melissa and Bill to join me at a small conference table in the corner. We all sit down together.

"Okay. Our purpose as a team is to figure out ways to reinforce our principle of sharing information and keeping people well-informed. As you know, we're one of four teams empowered to start changing things around here." They both look at me as if they've heard this speech a hundred times before. "So where do you think we should begin?"

Bill and Melissa look at each other. Finally, Bill breaks the ice.

"Maybe we should start by determining what kind of information we want to share. I mean, this is a pretty broad topic." Bill appears to be genuinely frustrated.

"Well, we know we're going to have to share our new mission statement and guiding principles," Melissa says. "Why don't we start with that?"

"What about what Wayne and Rock said about people laughing at it, though?" Bill interjects. "That kind of information isn't going to carry much weight without proof."

"That's true, Bill," I add. "Maybe we should start thinking

about alternative ways to communicate our principles."

"What do you mean by that?" Melissa asks.

"Well, I've been giving this a lot of thought lately," I reply. "And I don't think telling people what we're doing will have the same impact as showing them." I pause. "Let me ask you this. What do you think has more impact - what we say or what we do?"

"What we do," they both confirm at the same time.

"That's right. So telling people what our principles are will probably not have much impact. In fact, it may even be insulting. We need to figure out ways to show them."

"How do you suggest we do that?" Bill asks.

"I don't know," I admit. "I just know that's *what* we have to do. *How* we accomplish it is an entirely different story. That's what this team is supposed to figure out."

"What I hear you saying, Jack, is that we should concentrate more on our 'walk' than on our 'talk'," Melissa says, referring to a phrase I now use quite often.

"You mean our systems and procedures?" Bill asks.

"That's exactly what I mean," Melissa replies. "We have to figure out a way to bring our systems and procedures in line with all of our principles - not just one of them. It's like Nancy said - this is going to mean real change."

As Melissa says this, I hear the voice of Jordan. "The next step is alignment," he had advised. "This includes systems, as well as people. Form your teams around your systems and procedures, *not* around your principles."

"So by concentrating on just one principle - in our case, sharing information - we're probably going about it backwards?" I question.

"It sure seems that way to me," Melissa replies. "Doesn't it make more sense to form teams around specific actions - like reengineering a particular process - instead of broad issues like communication and involvement. We'd certainly see more tangible results."

"And we'd probably argue less," Bill adds.

"In other words, we're polarizing the teams around broad principles, rather than integrating them around specific cross-functional actions and processes," I say.

"That's right," Melissa replies. "The principles are the 'talk'. The actions are the 'walk'."

"Which means that initially we don't even have to 'talk the talk'," I add. "We just have to 'walk the walk'."

"Bingo," Melissa blurts out. "By changing some of our systems and operating procedures, people will discover for themselves what our principles are. They'll see proof. It's the only way to challenge their assumptions effectively. Otherwise, even the teams will see this as just a bunch of idealistic puff."

"I've already heard evidence of that," Bill sighs.

So this is what Jordan meant by warning me to focus our teams on systems and procedures, rather than on our principles. It does make a difference. "We are what we repeatedly do." By getting teams to change our existing systems - using our principles as a reference point - we create evidence of our commitment. We give people something tangible.

"And it gives us the opportunity to get a lot more people involved," I add. "Just think about how many procedures we have in this place."

"Or don't have," Melissa replies. "It's like Rock said the other day. We have people doing the same task six different ways. If you ask me, we're in desperate need of some standard operating procedures."

"Which is exactly what some of our customers have been telling us," I admit. I can feel things starting to come together.

"I suppose this creates a lot of room for teamwork," Bill says.

"Which would be another demonstration of one of our principles," Melissa adds. "We could use teams to align our systems with our principles."

I can feel some excitement building in the room as Melissa says this. It's like we just discovered a fundamental truth leading to massive opportunity for involvement and productive action, not to mention organizational integrity. By forming cross-functional teams around specific processes and empowering people to rethink the way we do things, we activate almost all of our principles simultaneously.

"So where do we go from here?" Bill asks. "If it's specific systems we should be focusing on instead of principles, aren't the teams we just set up heading in the wrong direction?"

"It certainly seems that way," I reply. They both look at me.

"Maybe you should draft a memo explaining our new direction to everyone?" Bill offers. "Otherwise, the teams are going to end up wasting a lot of valuable time."

"And it will cost this whole initiative a lot of credibility," Melissa adds. "It's a good thing we discovered this trap early on. We could have spent weeks spinning our wheels and getting nowhere."

"No memos," I reply firmly. "This is something we need to meet about and discuss face-to-face. In fact, from now on, I don't want memos used as a *first* means of communication."

They both look at me curiously.

"What do you mean by that?" Bill questions.

"I mean, if we have something to say to one another, we're going to start saying it in person," I explain. "Memos should only be used as follow-up."

"What if we have something to say to the whole plant?" Melissa asks.

"Then we'll say it through our plant manager and first line

supervisors. And they will be responsible for personally explaining whatever it is that we're trying to communcicate."

"Wow," Melissa replies. "That's certainly going to be different."

"Yeah, but it's another action that reinforces our principles," Bill admits. "It encourages us to talk to one another and listen with an open mind."

"Well, we're probably going to have to work on the open mind part," I reply. "But, you're right, Bill. At least, it promotes more listening and interaction. Consider it one of the first systems we change around here to reinforce our principles."

"Do you really think Wayne is going to take the time to explain things to his people face-to-face?" Melissa asks.

"When we start measuring it, he's going to have to," I reply. "That is, of course, if he plans to stay here."

Melissa and Bill are both silent for a moment. By the looks on their faces, they probably never expected me to confront Wayne on something like this. They both know of our long-term friendship and social ties. Personally, I find Wayne to be a lot of fun when he's away from the plant. I admit that he's a bit abrasive at work, but at home he's out-going, funny and full of life. And his wife, Annette, is the same way. Walking my talk with Wayne certainly isn't going to be easy.

"So what do you think we should do," Melissa asks. "Meet again with the staff and redefine our direction?"

"That's exactly what I think we should do," I reply. "And before we meet, we should probably have everyone identify a system that's out of whack."

"Like problems we have?" Bill asks.

"Recurring problems," I reply. "If it's recurring, there's probably something wrong with the system."

"Geez," Bill adds. "I can think of several already."

"So can I," Melissa adds. "This is going to be interesting."

"There's one other thing I think we need to focus some attention on," I add.

"What's that?" Bill asks.

"I think it's time we redefine our competition in terms that everyone in the organization can relate to."

"How are we going to do that?" Melissa asks.

"Think about it," I say. "If our mission is to get people to rave about us, what do you suppose our competition is?"

Melissa and Bill both gaze at me with puzzled looks on their faces.

"It's not what you would ordinarily think of as competition," I hint, thinking back to my own narrow perspective with my eleven year-old daughter, Kathleen. "Imagine for a moment that we're on a lifelong journey of on-going improvement - like a team of musicians in an orchestra. What are the forces against us?"

"The forces against us are probably the forces we place on ourselves," Melissa says. "It's anything we do to limit ourselves."

"Or move us in the wrong direction," I add.

"So anything that moves us in the opposite direction of our mission is our competition?" Bill asks.

"You tell me," I reply. "If our mission is to get people to rave about us, wouldn't you consider anything we do that gets people to complain about us to be our enemy."

"I never really thought about it that way," Bill admits. "But it does make sense."

"Wow," Melissa adds. "That is a different way to think about our competition."

"So it's like Nancy said the other day," Bill continues. "Everything from late shipments and inaccurate piececounts to incomplete labels and inaccurate invoices would be considered our competition. They all move us in the wrong direction."

"Not to mention things like personal injuries and poor treatment of our people," Melissa says. "This really brings some of the everyday annoyances we face into the light."

"That's right," I explain. "And it brings the competition a lot closer to the producers on the front line."

"That's for sure," Melissa says. "I'll bet if we asked some of the people out on the floor who our competition is right now, they wouldn't have a clue."

"Not to mention the people in the office," Bill adds.

"I've already asked some of them," I interject. "And you're both right. Our people have no idea who or what our real competition is. They consider the competition to be a Management problem." I stop and look from Bill to Melissa. "Yet, this new definition of our competition applies to everyone in the organization. It gives us something we actually have some control over."

"I suppose this means that we're going to have to get everyone in the company to buy into it," Melissa adds.

"That's how I see it," I confirm. "What do you think, Bill?"

"I agree," Bill replies. "If we're ever going to get people to rave about us as an organization, we're going to have to stop doing the things that people complain about. And that's going to require total participation from everyone."

As Bill says this, I remember something Jordan suggested in his workshop. "Look at things from opposite directions," he had said. "It creates interest and strengthens understanding. If your goal is to work smarter, for example, then ask your people to tell you about all the dumb things you do. This helps you to identify your competition."

"So how would you two suggest we get started?" I ask.

"Well, first of all, I think we need to cover this with the rest of the staff," Melissa says. "I suspect they're thinking along the same lines I was. They probably see our competition as some external company we bid against."

"And once we define our competition in this new way, we should probably start identifying all of the things that we do that cause complaints or limit us in any way," Bill adds. "And that includes internal complaints, as well as external complaints."

"This will give us plenty of specific projects to work on as teams," Melissa interjects. "If you ask me, we're going to be quite busy for awhile."

"You're probably right, Melissa. But this will be proactive, preventive activity - not reactive firefighting," I add. "This is exactly what we want to use teams for. Rather than continuing to run around pointing fingers, we'll use teams to pull things together by coming up with some synergistic, consistent procedures. This should eliminate all kinds of problems and unproductive activity."

"Will this mean that the teams have to be cross-functional in nature?" Bill asks.

"That will depend on the process. Some procedures will involve multiple functions or tasks. Others may involve only a single task."

"So, for example, if we form a team to come up with a procedure on how to pay invoices, we only need to involve the people who actually pay invoices, right?" Bill asks.

"Not necessarily," I respond. "We may have the wrong function paying invoices."

"And if we're trying to solve a problem involving inaccurate labels, we'll probably have to involve people from several departments?" Melissa asks.

"That's right."

"Come to think of it," Melissa interjects. "We could probably reengineer our entire labor agreement and employee handbook. I'll bet some of our people systems date back to the 1950's."

"That's for sure," Bill confirms.

"Okay, so rather than form teams around our principles," I conclude. "We'll form cross-functional teams around our problems - or anticipated problems - in relation to our mission statement, our guiding principles, and our true competition. This will keep the teams focused on our systems and processes and give us more tangible results." I pause and look curiously at my colleagues. "Does this make sense to you?"

"Makes a lot of sense to me," Melissa replies. "It gives the teams a stated purpose and allows them to dissolve once their task is complete."

"It's different," Bill adds. "But it's hard to argue with."

"Good," I conclude. "Then I'll call a meeting for later this week to go over these plans with the rest of the staff. In the meantime, I would like both of you to identify at least one process to start with."

"Sounds good to me," Melissa says. "I'll be ready."

"I'm already ready," Bill adds. "The more I think about it, the more I realize that we've become our own worst enemies. We've designed teamwork right out of this company."

So that's what Jordan meant when he said our true competition is right in front of us. When it comes to fulfilling a mission, it's actually within us.

PART IV

Challenge Your Assumptions

CHAPTER 14

"You were right," I say, looking across the small cafe table. "It does make a difference."

"What do you mean?" Jordan replies, taking a sip of his coffee.

"By forming teams around broad concepts like our guiding principles, we were confusing people. The whole project was losing momentum."

"It's a lesson a lot of companies learn after the fact," the man says casually.

"And I suppose it's a lesson you would have let me learn the hard way?"

"Sometimes that's the best way to learn." Jordan leans back and sips his coffee. "Tell me something, Jack. Do you suppose the kind of advice I offer is routinely dismissed by people?"

"Yeah, I imagine it is. I'll bet you run into a lot of know-it-all personalities." I stop and take a large bite out of my English muffin.

"But they listen to failure," he interjects. "They may not admit it, but they do hear it."

"So by planting seeds and allowing people to discover the truth for themselves, you gain credibility."

"That's right," he explains. "And in my business, I cannot be effective without credibility. It's a critical element in the art of persuasion."

"But isn't it difficult for you to let your clients fail?" I ask, wiping the corners of my mouth with my napkin.

"I don't see it that way," Jordan explains. "In fact, I see failure as the essence of success. Without the one, you cannot truly have the other."

"Why do you say that?"

"Because overcoming adversity is what builds inner strength. And it takes inner strength to be successful." He pauses and smiles. "Besides, I don't know all the answers. I only know that if you violate a moral principle, there is a price to pay. You become your own worst enemy."

"That sounds like something one of our managers said."

"It's true. Ask any group of people to tell you what demotivates them, and they'll say essentially the same thing you said a couple of months ago. People don't like to be treated in a dishonest manner. They don't like to be controlled. They don't like to be kept in the dark. They don't like to be treated with disrespect. They don't like to be subjected to an environment where they cannot grow - even if they don't seem to want to grow. These are violations of moral principles."

"Is this what you meant by our true competition?" I ask.

"Your true competition is anything you do that limits you or moves you in the wrong direction. Many of these forces are within each one of us, and they are the only thing we really have any control over."

"Is this why you allow your clients to make mistakes?" I ask.

Jordan pauses and sips his coffee.

"First of all, I don't think of the organizations I work with as clients. I view them as people - equal to myself. If they want my opinion, I'll share it. I won't force it. I'll give them the facts and I'll help them explore options. If they trust me, they can use my advice. This becomes their decision, not mine. If they don't agree with me, they can do whatever they want - no hard feelings. I encourage them to be skeptical. You see, Jack, my objective is to help people to grow. It's not to get them to do things my way."

"I can appreciate that."

"So, fill me in on your progress. It sounds like things are beginning to come together."

"Maybe at a snail's pace," I mumble. "Once we discovered that our original teams were heading in the wrong direction - by focusing solely on one principle - we created an all-purpose action team. It includes representatives from every department in the company. It's purpose is to lead satellite teams on specific actions."

"Sounds like a wise move." Jordan replies, sipping his coffee. "Tell me how you discovered you were heading in the wrong direction?"

"Well, after you planted the seed about aligning our systems and procedures with our principles, a few of us discovered that we had bitten off more than we could chew. We were trying to tackle the whole issue of communication and information-sharing without any clear-cut goals. And no one was raving. Ranting, maybe, but not raving."

"Not an uncommon mistake."

"So we called another meeting with all of the managers - and the union steward - to refocus our activity. As it turns out, we weren't the only team confused about what to do. This led to a very healthy discussion about process reengineering."

"And did you leave the meeting with a general consensus on how to proceed?"

"Most of the management team sees this as a great opportunity," I reply. "I explained it the same way you did to me."

"And what about the others?"

"Well, I was going to ask you about that?" I continue. "It seems this whole issue of reengineering really scares some people."

"Of course it does," Jordan says. "It exposes people. It means starting all over again. A lot of people view it as losing what they've already gained."

"That's why I wonder if it's right."

"That depends on the cost of the gain." The agent of change leans forward and puts both elbows on the table. "If what they have gained has come at a cost to others in your organization, it is indeed right. You have to think of your organization as a unit. If one individual, or department, gains at a cost to another, what happens to the net result?"

"Ultimately, it suffers."

"And when net results suffer, who pays for them?"

"We all do," I answer. "Our customers, our shareholders, our employees - we all pay for poor bottom line performance."

"Do your managers?"

"What do you mean?"

"When you take a turn for the worse, do any of your managers get laid off or see a decrease in compensation?"

"No, not really."

"So there is no consequence to your managers for poor performance?"

"I suppose not," I answer. "Unless, I fire them."

"Have you fired anyone in management lately because of poor performance?"

"No, not lately."

"In other words, a poor decision by a manager could cost dozens of people their jobs - with no consequence to the manager?"

"What are you suggesting?" I ask.

"One of the biggest voids in corporate America is the absence of consequence in the management ranks," he explains, leaning back in his chair. "Let's face it, Management has not been accountable to the people. Try turning the situation around. How many of your producers would honestly hire their boss to lead them?"

I laugh.

"So by reengineering, we're making Management more accountable to the producers?"

"That's part of it. You're also making the producers more accountable to one another and to their customers. You're putting accountability where it belongs. And you should. Accountability breeds quality and productivity. It also scares a lot of people because it exposes them."

The man looks at me. By the reflection in his eyes, I'm sure my face paints the picture of a man searching for answers.

"Here, let me explain it this way." He reaches for a blank index card from his shirt pocket and places it on the table. On the left side of the index card, he draws a triangle. At the top of the triangle, he colors in a small section and writes the words "Management Responsible" next to it. From here, he draws an arrow pointing straight down to the base of the triangle where he writes the words "Worker Responsive."

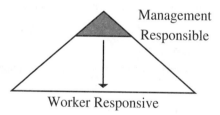

"Most organizations operate under the premise that the producers on the front line have to be told what to do and how to do it. Information flows at them - not from them - and they are accountable to supervisors who are accountable to managers who are accountable, ultimately, to a board of directors and a group of shareholders. In other words, the people on the line are expected to respond to Management's commands. The chain is vertical."

"That's certainly true in our case."

"So tell me, where does the customer come into this chain of command?" he asks.

"Well, I suppose the customer comes in somewhere near the bottom," I reply. "It's generally the producers on the line who have the most direct impact on the customer."

"In other words, the customer comes in last. They respond to you just like the people on the front line."

"Why do you say that?"

"Because that's the system you have in place." The man pauses. "Imagine you work out in your own Maintenance Shop. Under this structure, who are you accountable to?"

"My boss," I reply.

"And who is your boss accountable to?"

"His boss."

"Yet, who is your customer?"

"The people in production."

"And to what extent are you accountable to them?"

"Under our present system, I suppose I'm not really accountable at all." As I say this, I think about how often our people in production complain about the lousy service they get from our Maintenance personnel.

"So what happens if a person in production has a complaint?"

"They usually complain to their supervisor," I reply.

"And where does the complaint go from there?"

"I see your point," I admit. "The complaints go *up*. We're attempting to solve problems too high up in the organization - at the Management level - and that includes customer compaints, as well."

"There you go," Jordan says. "You're doing exactly what most American corporations are doing. You're holding people accountable to Management rather than to their customers. This makes Management responsible for solving all of your problems."

Jordan's right. I've been complaining about that for years.

"So how do you reverse this?" I ask after a long silence.

Without saying a word, Jordan now draws an inverted triangle on the right side of the index card. This time, he writes the words 'Worker Responsible' at the top and 'Management Responsive' at the bottom.

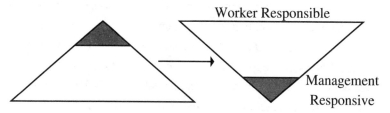

"Have you ever heard of the term 'paradigm shift'?" he asks.

"Yeah, I've heard it a lot," I respond. "Although, I've never really heard anyone define it very well."

"A paradigm shift is an awakening," Jordan explains. "It's what happens, for example, when what you think is true is suddenly proven false."

"In other words, it's like going back to zero again?"

"Exactly. A paradigm shift sends everyone back to zero again. It means that one of your basic assumptions was proven to be invalid."

"So is this an example of a paradigm shift?"

"This is a classic example," he replies. "This model reverses two-hundred years of thinking in American management."

"How is that?" I probe.

"To begin with, it recognizes that the producers on the front line have the potential to manage themselves."

"Like self-managed work teams?"

"Something like that. But you don't have to be on a team to manage yourself. People manage themselves everyday. Maybe not at TYPCO, but they do at home."

"I'm listening."

"In order for people to manage themselves - or teams, for that matter - they need to know exactly what is expected, they need to have guidance and support, and they need to know how they're doing."

"I remember you covering this with me earlier."

"Good," he smiles. "Don't forget it. They also need to understand accountability and consequence," he continues. "People are creatures of habit. They seek to gain pleasure and to avoid pain. Without consequence, which includes either pleasure or pain, they have no true direction. In other words, people need to know what *they* can expect, in addition to what is expected of them."

"So how is this a paradigm shift?"

"It's a shift in roles," he explains. "The people on the line take over more of management's traditional responsibilities, such as planning, organizing, controlling and problem-solving, and management takes on the role of process facilitator, mentor and coach."

"That doesn't sound like that much of a change," I rebut. "We've been training our managers and supervisors on coaching techniques for years."

"And have your systems changed as a result of it?" he counters.

"You mean our people systems?"

"Yes, your people systems."

I remember something Melissa said recently. She was suggesting that some of our people systems date back to the 1950's.

"I suppose some of our people systems are a bit antiquated," I admit.

"Is it possible, then, that your supervisors and managers are being trained and returned to systems that do not reinforce their roles as coaches?"

"Yes, I suppose that's true."

"Then I doubt you're getting much out of your training investment."

"You're probably right," I admit. My mind drifts quickly to Wayne. I wonder how many seminars he's attended on improving his people skills?

"Of course, there's a lot more to it than just coaching."

"What do you mean?"

"As you shift more responsibility, accountability and consequence to the producers on the line, and teach them to manage themselves within certain functions, Management must learn to coordinate the functions with one another." Jordan stops and sips his coffee. "Remember, it's the relationships between the functions that matter the most."

"Kind of like having a receiver who knows how to catch the football," I say.

"There you go." Jordan takes another index card from his shirt pocket and quickly sketches four tall rectangles on it. "Let's consider each one of these silos a function in your organization," he continues. "In fact, let's give them a name."

The man pauses and looks at me.

"Since we're having so much trouble fulfilling orders accurately, how about if we call one of them Shipping?" I offer.

"Good," he replies. "And that means we need to include the people who take the order, the people who schedule it and the people who make it."

He writes the words Customer Service in one silo, Scheduling in another, Production in the third and Shipping in the fourth silo.

"These four functions all contribute to fulfilling orders, right?"

"Yeah, that pretty much covers it," I confirm. "Customer

| Customer Service | Scheduling | Production | Shipping |

Service receives the orders, Scheduling schedules them, Production makes them, and Shipping ships them."

"And each function reports to a functional manager, right?"

"That's right. We have a manager in charge of each area."

"So tell me, who is in charge of the process?"

"You mean all four functions combined?" I say.

"Yes," he confirms. "Who is responsible for making sure that these four functions work together in the customer's best interest?"

"Other than myself, we don't really have anyone in charge of the whole process," I admit.

There is a long pause as Jordan sips his coffee and stares at me.

"Is there conflict between these areas?" he finally asks.

"Almost daily," I reply.

"And no one is responsible for managing this overall process in an optimal manner?"

"Are you suggesting that we restructure?"

"Tell me something, Jack. Does this conflict have any impact on your customers?"

Again, there is a long silence.

"So, by reengineering, you're saying we should rethink our organizational structure, as well as our systems?"

"I'm suggesting that you look for ways to tie accountability into your *processes,* not just the *functions* by themselves." As he says this, he takes his pen and draws an oval connecting the four pillars. Inside the oval, he scribbles the word "Process."

"Remember, it's the processes that matter the most to your customers, not the tasks by themselves."

"Doesn't this complicate people's individual responsibilities?"

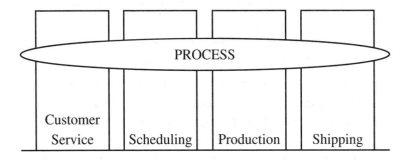

"Yes it does. But it simplifies the process. You have to make a choice."

"What do you mean?

"Think about it, Jack. Let's say you're running a small grocery store and you needed someone to sweep the floors."

"Okay."

"So you hire a part-time kid to come in and sweep the floors each day. And you pay him a wage for it, right?"

I nod my consent.

"As time passes, you discover that you could use some help stocking shelves," he adds. "So you go out and hire another part-time kid who specializes in stocking shelves, right?"

"No. I train the floor sweeper to stock the shelves and I pay him a little more money for it."

"Isn't that complicating his function as a specialist in floor sweeping?" The man smiles.

"I get your point. In an effort to simplify tasks, we've actually complicated processes."

"And limited the producers. If you ask me, the whole *division of labor* paradigm assumes that people can only be good at one thing."

"So this is what you meant when you said that most organizations have designed teamwork right out of their culture?"

"It sure appears that way to me. Most companies have put up walls between functions - leading to separation and fragmentation. You even fell into the same trap by trying to set up your teams around individual principles, rather than integrating all of your principles into your operating processes. Today, this paradigm is no longer acceptable. It isolates people and creates barriers to achieving synergistic results. To create a high performance work environment, you have to expose people to the big picture. This leaves the door wide open for massive reengineering. Rest assured, this is an awakening to most conventional thinkers."

As we talk, a waitress walks over and asks us if there will be anything else. I look to Jordan.

"I really have to run," he says politely. "Thank you."

"I'm the one who should be saying 'thank you'," I whisper as I collect the bill. "At some point, we're going to have to discuss your fee. I trust I owe you a great deal more than breakfast."

"We can discuss that some other time," he says as he stands up. "For now, consider it an addendum to the workshop."

"I appreciate that," I say as I stand and shake the man's hand.

"By the way," he quips. "Make sure that when your action team sets out to rethink your systems, you start with a blank piece of paper." He smiles. "And one more thing - rather than concentrate on how you can do what you do better, think about why you do what you do at all?"

"I'll do that," I reply as the man walks away. There he goes again. He plants a seed and then disappears - only to return later to nurture the growth process. I collect the two index cards left on the table - a tip for me, I trust - and I head for TYPCO, wondering why do we do what we do at all.

CHAPTER 15

A s I arrive at work, I can't help but think about what Jordan said. Reengineering is a paradigm shift. It's an awakening. And, by beginning with a blank piece of paper, we force ourselves to rethink our systems as if they never existed. We go beyond asking how we can improve what we're already doing. Instead, we challenge the need to do it at all. We expose the busywork and declutter the process.

"Good morning, Jack," my secretary says, as I walk toward my office.

"Good morning, Lisa," I reply. "What's the news?"

"Well, Jim Rockwell wants to see you when you get a moment." She hands me a note. "He stopped by about an hour ago. He said it wasn't anything urgent."

"Thanks, Lisa. Anything else?"

"No. That's it for now. Do you want me to page Jim?"

"No, thanks. I think I'll go track him down in the plant."

"Good luck," she says, as she spins back to the work in front of her.

I wonder what Rock wants to see me about. Normally, he takes care of matters with Melissa. He's probably got another gripe about Wayne. I toss my coat over a chair and head for the plant.

Ten minutes later, I find Rock standing next to one of our large injection presses.

"What's up?" I shout over the noise of the machinery.

"You got a minute?" he shouts back.

"Sure. Why don't we take a walk?" I suggest, figuring it might not be a bad idea for some of our producers to see me walking with Rock.

"Good idea. We won't have to yell so much."

I wait a few minutes while Rock gets himself organized. Meanwhile, I speculate on why he wants to see me.

"So what's up?" I finally ask.

"I want to run an idea by you."

"Go ahead, I'm listening." I shove both hands in my pockets.

"Well, I've been thinking a lot about this action team we set up," he continues. "And I don't think we really know what we're doing."

I keep walking without saying a word.

"Don't get me wrong," he explains. "I like the idea and everything. I'm just afraid this whole project is going to turn into another fad."

I stop and face Rock.

"Why do you say that?"

"Because most people around here don't really think anything will change. Even some of the people on the action team doubt Management's commitment."

"Do they doubt me?" I ask.

"They doubt some of the people you surround yourself with," the big man says. "And since you're the guy in charge, they consider you responsible."

"I was under the impression that the people who volunteered to be on the action team want to see things change." I start walking again slowly.

"They do," Rock explains. "They just wonder if they're wasting their time."

"I thought it was pretty clear that the action team was created to come up with a better way to do things."

"That true." Rock nods to a comrade on the line. "But I don't think our action team knows how to do that."

"What do you mean?"

"To begin with, we hardly even know each other. In fact, some of us just met for the first time. On top of that, we don't even know where to start. We've never done anything like this before."

"What if I said start with a blank piece of paper?"

"I'd wonder what you were talking about," he answers. "We need more guidance than that."

Rock is right. We have to *enable* people before we can *empower* them.

"So what do you suggest?" I ask.

"I think we should take the whole team off-site for a planning meeting. I really think it would help us get more focused."

"It sounds like people are telling you they're confused."

"You've got that right," he admits. "And I'm confused."

"What are you confused about?"

"Well, I understand the need for a mission statement and guiding principles. That much makes sense. But it's when we start getting into all this talk about redesign and alignment that I get confused. And, frankly, it makes a lot of people nervous."

"There's no doubt about that," I admit. "Even Wayne seems to be questioning his job security right now."

"Well, I can live with that," Rock laughs. "But I don't think it's your intention to scare the people on the line, is it?"

"No, I'm not trying to scare anyone on the line, Rock."

"Well, that isn't the message being heard," he advises. "The folks on the line think you're planning to use these principles to weed out the people you don't want."

"Do you believe that?"

"No," he answers. "I understand what you're trying to do. And I appreciate your bringing me in on the front end of this. But I think we have some explaining to do."

"So you think that by bringing our action team together for a day off-site we can build some positive momentum?"

"Yes, I do," Rock says. "And I've run the idea by a few other members on the team, and they agree with me."

Suddenly, a thought comes to my mind.

"Let me ask you this, Rock," I say. "What if we were to do what you're suggesting, but with an outside facilitator?"

"You mean like a teacher or something?"

"Yeah," I respond. "I know a guy who specializes in what we're trying to do. I'm sure he could be a great help to us."

"I think that's a super idea - as long as we walk away with a better understanding of what this is all about."

"Then let me see what I can do," I reply enthusiastically. "I think going off-site for a day is an excellent way to get the ball rolling. Thanks for the suggestion, Rock."

As I walk away, I ask myself, why don't I trust this guy? Rock's a decent person. He cares about what he's doing. In fact, he probably cares more than most people. Am I listening to the wrong people? Am I jumping to conclusions? Are my assumptions valid?

CHAPTER 16

As I head toward the hotel conference room, I reflect on the past three weeks. On the one hand, I'm excited about the positive reaction from the eighteen people who are joining me for the day. Rock is especially excited. Of course, it was his idea. I'm also excited about having Jordan join us for the day as our facilitator. I trust it will be well worth the fee - a fee I would have shuttered at only six months ago.

On the other hand, I'm a bit nervous. What if the whole thing flops? What if we go back to the plant and nothing changes? What if people see this as just another fad? My credibility will be shot. We'll be worse off than we were before. At least I'm not the one facilitating the workshop. Jordan certainly has his work cut out for him.

As I walk into the room, I see a few clusters of people standing around drinking coffee and telling stories. They look like packs of wolves, sticking together among their own kind - except for Jordan. He's right in the middle of one pack, listening attentively.

"Good morning," I say to a few people who see me as I enter the room.

"Good morning," comes a soft, unrehearsed reply.

"How does everything look?" I ask Jordan, as we meet in the center of the room to shake hands.

"Looks good!" he replies. "You have some very interesting people attending."

"Would you like me to introduce you around?" I ask.

"No, thanks. I'll just mingle."

"Is the room set up the way you want it?" I ask, looking around. There are four round tables with five chairs at each. There are two flip charts in the front of the room and a small table off to one side with a large duffle bag on it. In the back of the room, I see a long table with coffee, juice and danish scattered across it. There is no lectern or overhead projector in site. In my opinion, the room doesn't appear to be very well organized.

"It's perfect," he smiles. "I have everything I need."

"So what's your plan?" I ask.

"My plan is to get you to plan," he responds. "And to have a little fun doing it."

"Well, just let me know if there's anything I can do to help."

"I will," he replies. "For now, you can simply help me facilitate the process by making this as easy on people as possible. Remember, people are typically their own worst enemies - especially when faced with something new and different. Give them your attention and support."

"I'm with you."

"So let's split up and mingle," he suggests. "We still have fifteen minutes before we start. And the better I get to know people now, the easier it will be for me to get them to speak up later."

During the next fifteen minutes, the man weaves his way in and out of the growing packs of people scattered throughout the room. From where I'm standing, I can see the curious looks on people's faces as he walks away from them. I wonder what they're thinking. Will they actually take this guy seriously? I mean, here is a man dressed in a pair of beige khakis, a blue and white striped dress shirt, and a pair of scuffed loafers - not exactly the image of a professional consultant.

As the clock strikes eight, I stand up in the front of the room to call the meeting to order. After thanking everyone for attending, I begin my introduction.

"By now, you've probably already met our facilitator, Jordan McKay. I invited Mr. McKay to join us today as we begin to identify more proactive ways to move TYPCO in the direction of our mission." I pause. "Jordan requested that I not give him a real formal introduction, so I won't. Let me just say that we are very fortunate to have this man with us today. He is in great demand all over the world because of his keen insights on the subjects of leadership, teamwork, motivation and organizational behavior. He has clearly inspired me to challenge some of my own assumptions and to rethink my own behavior. Now I'm eager to share this experience with you. From here, we can begin to examine TYPCO's behavior in relation to our guiding principles and challenge the assumptions driving it." I stop and look around the room. The faces are frozen. Jordan is studying the people.

"I met Jordan about six months ago at a workshop he offered in Boston," I continue. "This triggered a series of conversations that led to the development of this action team. It is my opinion that we have some vast opportunity awaiting us - and we have a true master of the change process here to help us get started." I turn to the agent of change. "Please welcome Jordan McKay."

There is no applause.

Jordan walks up to one of the flip charts and starts drawing a picture. The room is silent. I laugh to myself. Evidently, his index cards aren't large enough for a group this size. Suddenly, he turns around, scans the faces in the room and smiles.

"How about if we begin with a little exercise?" he says. I immediately think of Confucius - *what I do, I understand.* The faces are still frozen. He continues.

"Without talking to anyone, please take a few minutes to figure out how many squares there are in this figure. When you have an answer, please write it down on a piece of paper."

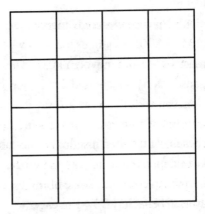

The ice breaks. A few people start laughing and looking around. Is this guy serious? What a stupid question. Or, maybe it's a trick question? How many squares?

Some people jot down an answer almost immediately. Others are deep in thought. Jordan strolls around the room, waiting patiently.

After a few minutes, it appears everyone has finished. Jordan walks back up to the flip chart, turns and faces the group.

"How many did you get, Sandy?" he asks.

"22," she replies. Jordan writes 22 at the top of the flip chart.

"How about you, Duane?" he continues. "How many did you get?"

"I got 26," he answers. Jordan writes 26 next to the 22.

"Melissa, how many did you come up with?" he asks.

"I came up with 24," she replies. Jordan adds 24 to the list. People are starting to pay more attention.

"Fred, what did you write down?" No wonder the man wanted to mingle. He must have spent the first half hour of the day memorizing everyone's name.

"I got the same as Melissa."

"Okay, how about you, Walt?" Walt is our Maintenance Manager.

"I wrote down 16," he says. Jordan writes 16 next to the 22, the 26, and the 24.

"Wayne, it's your turn," he continues. "How many did you get?

"I got 21." Jordan adds 21 to the list.

During the next few minutes, Jordan collects four additional answers and writes them all down next to the five he already has.

"What do you suppose this means?" he finally asks.

"I suspect it means that we can all look at the same thing and see something quite different," Melissa answers.

"That's right," he continues. "And what implications do you suppose this has on human relationships?"

"It often leads to conflict."

"Very good, Melissa," he continues. "And what is the source of that conflict?"

The room is silent.

"Walt, if you see 16 squares and Melissa sees 24 squares, what is the source of the conflict?"

"It's that we don't agree," he answers. "She sees it one way and I see it another."

"And what are you basing your perception on?" he probes. "Fact or assumption?"

"Do you mean do I know for a fact that there are sixteen squares?" Walt asks.

"That's right. Do you know for a fact that there are only 16 squares?"

"No," he answers. "I suppose that's an assumption I'm making."

"And what about you, Melissa?" Jordan turns toward Melissa. "Do you know for a fact that there are only 24 squares?"

"No," she replies. "That would be an assumption, as well."

"Very interesting," the man says. "It would appear that we have a lot of room for conflict here. Out of a group of 19 people, we came up with nine different answers - at least two of which we know are based on assumption." He pauses. "Yet some were ready to dismiss the exercise as trivial. Tell me something, how many of you would now be willing to bet that your answer is correct?"

Not a single hand goes up - even though two people in the room had written down 30, which is the correct answer.

"Let's try working through the exercise together," he continues. "First, let's define a square."

"A square has four equal sides," Sandy offers.

"And four right angles," Ray adds.

"Alright, then a one-by-one would qualify as a square, right?"

"Right," several people confirm at once.

"Okay, then how many one-by-one's are there in the figure?"

"16," comes a united reply.

"Good. And how about "two-by-two's?" he asks.

There is some confusion and disagreement.

"Think carefully," he hints. "Each two-by-two has an intersection and the squares overlap."

"There are nine," comes an unsynchronized reply.

"Very good," he continues. "Now how about three-by-three's?"

"That's where I screwed up," someone whispers.

"Four," several people shout at once.

"Alright," Jordan confirms. "And it's obvious there is only one four-by-four, so that gives us a total of 30 squares." He pauses and looks around the room. "Does anyone disagree?"

The room is quiet.

"Good. Then we have a consensus. We all agree." Jordan walks over to the other flip chart and quickly sketches a model.

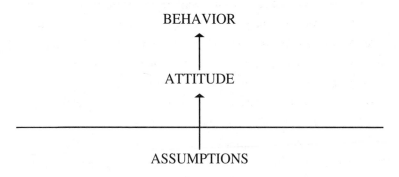

BEHAVIOR

↑

ATTITUDE

↑

ASSUMPTIONS

"The reason I wanted to start with this exercise is to create some interest in the relationship between assumptions and behavior. People make assumptions every day. And these assumptions influence our attitudes and our behavior. If our assumptions are flawed, our attitudes and behavior may be out of line." He stops and looks around the room. "Can anyone think of a time when they jumped to a conclusion without gathering the facts?"

I see a room full of heads bobbing up and down.

"I just did," Walt admits, referring to the exercise.

"So did I," several others whisper at the same time.

"Well, don't feel bad," Jordan replies. "It's a temptation that's hard to resist. We're accustomed to doing things in a hurry because we live in a fast-paced society. The important thing to remember is that when you're working with others, you must keep an open mind. You must distinguish facts from assumptions."

"How do we do that?" Melissa asks.

"You can start by asking one another if the information you have is based on fact or assumption," Jordan answers. "Seek first to understand."

"And if it's an assumption?" Walt asks.

"Be skeptical," the facilitator replies. "Why trust something you know may not be true?"

The man has an interesting way of getting people involved in a dialogue. He knows their names. He asks them questions. He creates images in their minds. He treats them with dignity. He makes learning fun.

"So, let's take a look at some of the assumptions you're making as a company," he continues. "What is driving your organization's behavior?"

In the next thirty minutes, we uncover at least a dozen powerful assumptions that appear to be flawed. We discover that we have the wrong people making hiring decisions and reviewing performance. We identify a multitude of systems that are built on the assumption that people cannot manage themselves. We find that we are without standard operating procedures in most of our operations. The more we look, the more we realize that we treat people as though they cannot make a responsible decision. It becomes painfully clear that we do not act as if we trust our people. And Jordan is doing nothing more than asking questions.

"How many of you are aware of your organization's new mission statement and guiding principles?" Jordan continues.

A few hands go up.

"Okay, Melissa," he says. "Can you help us out? What is your mission as an organization?"

"It's to get people to rave about us," she replies.

"And why is that important, Bill?" he quizzes.

"Well, we figure that if we can get people to rave about us, we will become stronger as a business," Bill answers. "This creates opportunity and security for all of us."

"It also gives us focus," Melissa adds. "Our customers will only rave about us if we go beyond what they expect. Our employees will only rave about us if we provide a truly superior place to work. Our shareholders will only rave about us if we provide them with excellent financial returns. Our real mission is to do whatever we have to do to get people to view us as an outstanding organization."

"Within certain guidelines," I interject.

Jordan looks to me.

"And what are those guidelines?" he asks.

"To guide us on our mission, we have identified twelve principles that we believe are critical to our success," I reply, standing up and grabbing a stack of papers. "Here is a summary of our mission statement and our guiding principles." I walk to each table and distribute the handouts. "I want each of you to have a copy."

People scan the handout quickly. Some have seen it before.

OUR MISSION

To get people to rave about us!

OUR GUIDING PRINCIPLES

1. <u>Think like the customer:</u> This principle is fundamental to our survival. Without customers, TYPCO cannot exist. To accomplish our mission, we must learn to think from our customer's point of view.

2. <u>Work cooperatively as a team:</u> The only way to achieve synergistic results is through teamwork. This principle reminds us that in order to achieve excellence, we must put the "we" in front of the "me."

3. <u>Keep people well informed:</u> Information is power. With it, people can act responsibly. Without it, people tend to shift responsibility to those who have it. This principle reminds us to ask for and share relevent information with one another.

4. <u>Commit to excellence and on-going improvement:</u> The only way to get people to rave about us is to stun them with results that go beyond their expectations. This requires on-going development of our people and a commitment to elevating our standards beyond the norm.

5. <u>Be honest:</u> Trust and integrity are critical to high performance teamwork. Honesty breeds trust. This principle reminds us to seek truth and to demonstrate integrity.

6. <u>Be consistent:</u> In a world of continuous change, people need a constant. These principles give us constancy of purpose.

7. <u>Involve people in decisions that impact their work:</u> People are less likely to argue with their own data. Involvement breeds commitment. This principle reminds us to view one another as valuable resources.

8. <u>Listen with an open mind:</u> Involving people in decisions makes no sense if we refuse to listen to alternative points of view. Listening creates a pathway to learning. This principle reminds us to challenge our assumptions with an open mind.

9. <u>Treat one another with dignity:</u> Committing to this principle builds self-esteem and inspires people to achieve higher levels of performance. Our real strength lies within us.

10. <u>Accept honest mistakes as learning opportunities:</u> Viewing mistakes as anything but constructive leaves us in the shadows of the brave. Take a risk. Be proactive. Dare to do what you believe is right.

11. <u>Be acccountable for your behavior:</u> Our mission cannot be accomplished without ownership. We must all take responsibility for being part of the solution, not part of the problem. These principles are intended to hold us together and move us in a common, united direction.

12. <u>Pull the weeds:</u> We define a weed as a plant out of place. It isn't, in and of itself, good or bad. It simply doesn't belong where it is. Left alone, it becomes an obstacle to synergistic performance and growth. We owe it to ourselves to confront these obstacles. Continuous violators of our principles will be removed.

"I can just imagine what Wayne thinks of these," one person whispers to another, well out of earshot of Wayne.

"That's for sure," comes the reply. "I'll believe this when I see it."

I ignore the comments.

"We believe that by aligning our systems and our people with these principles, we will begin to get people to rave about us." I pause and look around the room. "But it's going to mean a lot of change."

"What kind of change?" Mario asks. Mario is an hourly employee from Shipping.

"That's what this action team is empowered to find out," I reply. "Now that our mission statement and guiding principles are defined, the real work begins. Rest assured, I plan to hold everyone in Management accountable for working under these principles."

"How are we supposed to know what to do?" Rock asks.

"Well, that's why I asked Jordan to join us today," I explain. "He's here to help us get started."

"Good," Mario says. "We're going to need some help."

"What kind of help do you think you're going to need, Mario?" Jordan asks.

"Well, for one thing, I've never done anything like this before?" Mario explains.

"Is that right?" Jordan smiles, as if he knows something Mario does not. "You've never *planned* anything before?"

"I've planned a lot of things," Mario counters. "But I've never written procedures on anything."

"Have you ever been asked for directions on how to get someplace?" Jordan pulls.

"Sure," Mario answers. "But that's different."

"Why is that different?"

"Because I know how to give those kinds of directions."

"You work in Shipping, right?" Jordan continues.

"That's right," Mario replies.

"Do you know how to give directions in Shipping?"

"Sure. I've worked there for almost sixteen years."

"Good." Jordan smiles. "You'll be a valuable resource to the team. You know how to plan. And you know how to give directions in an important area of the business."

Mario looks stumped.

"Of course, there's a lot more to it than that," Jordan admits. "There is a rational way to plan, and there is an irrational way to plan. Naturally, we're going to want to do this rationally. Am I right?"

The heads all start bobbing again.

"Good," he continues. "Who knows the difference?"

"A rational plan would be a plan that makes sense, and an irrational plan would be a plan that doesn't make sense," Rock says.

"Sounds pretty easy, doesn't it?" Jordan asks. "But how will we know if it makes any sense if we haven't tested it out yet?"

"What if it's worked before?" Melissa asks.

"Does that make it the best plan for the future?" he challenges.

"Not necessarily, but it gives us some experience," Melissa adds.

"You're absolutely right," he confirms. "It gives us one option."

"So you're suggesting that we should look beyond the one option in search of a better way to do things?" Melissa asks.

"I'm glad you're a member of this action team, Melissa," he answers. "You catch on very quickly."

"So our goal as a team is to look for better ways to do things?" Ray says. Ray is a customer service representative.

"That's right," Jordan confirms. "And to document your

discoveries in the form of standard operating procedures."

"Why is that important?" Sandy asks. Sandy is a production scheduler.

"That's a good question, Sandy," the facilitatior replies. "In fact, I anticipated somebody might ask that." Jordan turns and walks over to his duffle bag. From it, he pulls out a VCR. He walks over to Sandy's table and places the VCR in front of her. He then stretches the extension cord across the room and plugs it in.

"Would you care to show the rest of us how to program the clock on this VCR?" he asks.

The room breaks into laughter. Sandy blushes.

"Do you have any instructions?" she asks shyly.

"What if I said no?"

"Then I would have to say no," she answers, looking the machine over.

"Why, Sandy?"

"Because I've never done it before, and I don't have anything that tells me how to do it," she says.

"Interesting," Jordan quips, folding his arms and drawing one hand up to his chin. He then walks over to his bag and pulls out a set of instructions. "How about if I give you these instructions?"

"That would probably help," Sandy assumes.

She takes the instructions and quickly reads the section on how to set the clock. Suddenly, she discovers something is wrong.

"I don't think these are the right instructions," she says.

"Why do you say that?"

"Because they apply to a different model," she laughs.

"I see," he concludes. "So having procedures only helps if they're accurate? Assuming otherwise could be dangerous."

He walks back over to his bag and pulls out a new set of instructions.

"How about if we try these?"

Sandy cautiously takes the instructions and within minutes she has figured out how to program the VCR's clock.

The room breaks into applause.

"How many of you are familiar with the term *empowerment?*" Jordan asks.

Nearly everyone's hand goes up.

"Is it fair to say, then, that I just empowered Sandy to do something she claimed she had never done before?"

A volley of "yes's" rings throughout the room.

"How did I do it?"

"You gave her the tools she needed to do it herself," Tim blurts out.

"That's right," Jordan confirms. "I gave Sandy the information and the responsibility to do it for herself. I gave her power. With it, she can do remarkable things. Without it, she becomes a victim of someone else's decisions. I will refer to this as self-management."

He walks over and picks up the VCR.

"Would anyone else like to try it?" he asks.

The room is silent.

"Good," he says. "We have more important things to do now, anyway. What I want you to remember, though, is that you are capable of doing much more than you think. Seize the opportunities that await you."

The rest of the day raced by. Jordan had us working with tinker toys, blindfolds, tennis balls and a rational problem-solving exercise. At one point, he even had us listen to ourselves solve a problem using audio tape feedback. There was no doubt in anyone's mind that the assumptions we tend to make can severely limit our behavior.

By the end of the day, the walls were covered with flip chart paper identifying specific TYPCO processes that needed to be reexamined. Using our principles as a reference, we found that our people systems, our customer service systems, our information systems, our facilities management systems, our procurement systems, our quality assurance systems and our manufacturing systems could all use an overhaul. To be perfectly honest, we discovered that there was very little in our organization that shouldn't change in one way or another.

The interesting thing was that nearly everyone in the workshop left looking forward to it. I was stunned. I mean, here we are talking about changing nearly everything in the organization and people are *excited* about it. Even Wayne and Steve showed signs of hope.

As for Jordan, the man clearly pulled things together. He knew where we needed to go, and he knew how to get us there. Every time someone challenged him on something, he was prepared. It was as if he knew in advance what their arguments would be. But he never talked down to anyone. He simply inspired them to question their own assumptions. At times, he would tell stories and offer examples. Other times, he would use an exercise to demonstrate his point. In either case, he kept us actively engaged in the learning process.

In the end, we all walked away with clear *goals* and clear *roles*. Every member of the action team is now responsible for doing something. Melissa, for example, is pulling together a team to reengineer our performance review process. Mark is coordinating a team to reexamine our procurement process. Nancy is leading a team on rethinking our order fulfillment process. Rock is pulling together a team to look at ways to cross-train our production operators. Bill is recruiting some people to rethink our financial reporting procedures. Wayne is putting a team together to focus on reducing waste. Walt is pulling some people together to explore ways to improve the relationship between our Skilled Trades personnel and our production operators. And I am pulling together a team to figure out how to measure the quality of our leadership. Jordan helped us get focused. Now, it's up to us to follow through.

PART V

Confront Your Fears

CHAPTER 17

A s I head toward Melissa's office, I reflect on some of the things she quizzed me on earlier. How is her team supposed to create and implement a new performance management system without Wayne's commitment - especially one that requires peer performance reviews?

I'm greeted at the door by Rock, Mario, Ray, Sandy, Tim and, of course, Melissa. Evidentally, she invited the whole team to attend the meeting. They've been working on this project now for about three weeks, one hour per day. The system they've come up with is nearly complete. In fact, it dovetails with the system my own team has come up with on measuring the quality of our leadership. Since Melissa is a member of both teams, she's coordinated the two systems nicely.

"So what's the trouble," I ask.

"Well," Melissa begins. "We're concerned that our new performance management system is going to backfire if we don't have a genuine commitment from all of our managers." She pauses and looks around the room. "And our two major stumbling blocks are Wayne and Steve."

"Why do you say that?"

"Before putting this new system together, we spent time in each department talking with the managers and a random group of their people," she explains. "We did this to determine up front what was most important to the people, and to gather ideas on how to measure it."

"Go on."

"The two most critical questions we asked were: What criteria is most important to you in terms of feedback, and who is in the best position to provide the feedback?" Melissa stops and looks over at Rock. "We got excellent cooperation, with the exception of Wayne and Steve."

"Can you give me an example?" I probe.

"I can give you several," she explains. "Most of the managers see this as a real opportunity. They understand the value in giving people visible goals and meaningful feedback." She pauses. "It's like Jordan demonstrated a couple of weeks ago with the blindfolds. By removing them, people are capable of doing so much more, especially when they are accountable to one another."

"And Wayne and Steve don't see it this way?" I question.

"Basically, they just told us to do whatever we want," Rock interjects.

"So what have you done?"

"We went ahead and designed a new system based on the information we have," Melissa replies. "It's all we could do."

"And now?" I question.

"Now, we're concerned that Wayne and Steve will kill it," Rock says.

"Have you presented it to them yet?"

"No. That's our next step," Melissa answers. "We have a presentation prepared for next week. We're in the process of scheduling it now."

"Who do you plan to invite?"

"We plan to invite all of the managers and supervisors," Melissa replies. "Since this is going to affect everyone in the organization, we decided to start with the people who have to facilitate it."

"And you're concerned about Wayne and Steve following through?" I ask.

"Yes," Melissa confirms. "We are."

"How do you feel about it, Tim," I ask, looking over at the young man on my right. "You work out on the production floor."

"I agree with Rock and Melissa," he responds. "If Wayne doesn't back us up on this, people will just blow it off."

"How about you, Ray?" I turn toward Ray. "You speak for the Customer Service department."

"We have the same problem the plant has," he explains. "We have a commitment from Nancy. But without a commitment from Steve, this whole project could fail."

I look around the room. There is genuine concern in the eyes staring at me. These people are looking for a commitment from me.

"What do you want me to do?" I ask.

"First, we need to know that you're committed to this," Melissa interjects. "Second, we need to know that Wayne and Steve, along with the rest of us, will be held accountable for making this work."

All eyes are still on me.

"Let me begin by stating very clearly that I am committed to our mission and guiding principles. We've invested a great deal of time, energy and money in this initiative, and I intend to make it work." I stop and make eye contact with each member of the team. "Assuming your presentation is good, and your new system is sound, you will have my support."

"And if the system isn't something you like?" Rock asks.

"Why wouldn't I like it if you've taken my interests into consideration?" The room is silent as the team members turn and look at one another. "Isn't that what win/win negotiation is all about - looking out for one another's interests?"

I realize my question is unexpected, but I'm trying to make a point. I want our people to start looking out for one another. I want them to bring our mission statement and guiding principles to life. I want them to begin writing business plans that take the entire division into consideration. Melissa breaks the silence.

"Can we ask what your interests are?"

"Think about it, Melissa." I smile reassuringly. "I've just given you the answer."

CHAPTER 18

As I leave Melissa's office, I decide to drop in on Wayne. My instincts about Wayne are now proving to be more and more valid. Given that Melissa's team has designed a new performance management system that is in alignment with our mission and guiding principles, I see no reason why I would dispute it. Wayne, however, is another matter. He's had trouble buying into our new management philosophy from day one.

Naturally, I find Wayne in his office. He spends little time anywhere else, other than in meetings.

"Got a minute," I ask, leaning my head in through the doorway.

"I always have a minute for you, Jack," he replies in his rugged style. "Come on in."

I walk in and close the door behind me.

"How's your team coming along?" I ask, sitting down. "Are you putting together some ideas on how to reduce waste around here?"

Wayne hesitates.

"Actually, I'm having trouble getting people to take this seriously," he replies. "It's like I said before, a lot of folks just consider this another charade."

"How often do you meet?" I pull.

"We tried meeting last week, but only a few people showed

up. I'm trying to set up another meeting now."

"When?" Wayne's excuses are running out.

"Probably next week sometime. I'll let you know."

"Please do. I'd like to attend it myself."

Wayne realizes I see through his weak excuses and ineffective leadership style. He doesn't get people to volunteer and take the matter seriously because he has no credibility with his people. The topic could be World War III and still no one would rally around Wayne.

"How about this new performance management system that Melissa and her team are designing?" I probe. "Tell me what you think about that?"

"Well, I don't know much about it," he grunts. "So I can't really say."

"Have you been asked about it?"

"Yeah," he admits. "I've been asked about it."

"And what did you recommend?" I continue.

"I told them to do whatever they think is right," he snorts.

"And you're ready to buy into whatever they come up with?"

"That depends on what they come up with, Jack," he says, leaning back in his chair. "I assume you feel the same way."

"Let's be careful about what we assume, Wayne." I pause and look at him intently. "Would you like to know how I really feel about it?"

"Sure," he huffs. "Spill your guts."

"Well, to put it simply, I'm prepared to commit to whatever they come up with, as long as it's in line with our mission and guiding principles."

"But what if it's wrong?" Wayne snaps.

I pause for a moment to avoid a spitting match.

"Wrong in relation to what?" I finally ask quietly.

He hesitates. I can see him searching for an answer.

"What if this new system screws everything up?"

"Then it will obviously have to be amended," I reply. "Is that so bad?"

"I don't know, Jack," he growls. "I have a bad feeling about this."

"Why is that, Wayne?"

"It's just so radically different from what we've always done," he explains. "It seems like the whole company is flipping upside down. I mean, first, your team comes up with a - what do you call it - a LAP?

"A Leadership Assessment Profile," I clarify.

"That's right," he continues. "A Leadership Assessment Profile to measure our performance as leaders. And now Melissa is coming up with a way for people to provide feedback to one another." He stops and shakes his head. "It just seems like we're complicating a lot of things. I mean, the paperwork alone is going to be a nightmare."

"Is that a fact or an assumption?" I ask, mirroring Jordan's style.

"What do you mean?"

"Your statement about complicating things with a lot of paperwork," I repeat. "Are you assuming that there will be more paperwork, or do you know that for a fact?"

"Well, I don't see how we can do it without creating more work," Wayne proclaims.

"That sounds like an assumption to me, Wayne," I state firmly. "And we've promised to keep an open mind and challenge our assumptions."

"You aren't going to let me forget those principles, are you?"

"No. And I'll tell you why. I believe that by commiting to those principles, we have the potential to unleash power that we don't even know we have. And I'm determined to do that. We're going to become the leading division within TYPCO."

"So you think those principles are going to give us strength?"

"Something has to pull us together as a team. And that's the only way we can achieve synergistic results."

"What about the people who want to take advantage of us? What do you plan to do about them?"

"Wayne, I've already seen evidence of people pulling together around our principles - even some of our skeptics. I wouldn't enter us in any races, but we're definitely picking up some momentum. Sooner or later, the remaining skeptics are going to find themselves without an audience. Besides, it's time we stop treating the 80% of our good people like the 20% of our troublemakers. Eventually, we'll pull the weeds."

"I see," he mutters.

"And, as for more paperwork, we're approaching this whole initiative with the concept of decluttering in mind. We're looking for ways to put accountability where it belongs so that we can eliminate excess layers of work." I pause and lean forward, placing both elbows on my knees. "Tell me something, Wayne. How would you feel if you were a production operator and you were suddenly given the opportunity to fill out a customer service card each time a mechanic had to service a machine you worked on?"

"I don't know," he says. "Wouldn't that create conflicts between Production and Maintenance?"

"It would if we forced it upon people. But if the people design the system themselves, and understand it's purpose, it becomes theirs to manage. It's no different than managing the conflicts we have now with our outside customers."

"Is there a system like that being developed?" Wayne asks.

"As a matter of fact, there is. Walt's team is designing a service feedback system for all of the people who work in Skilled Trades."

"And the production operators are going to be the ones who give the mechanics and welders and electricians feedback?"

"That's right," I confirm. "We plan to let the producers on the line manage the system themselves. Management will simply facilitate the process."

"Using what criteria?"

"Using a criteria that Walt's team is coming up with. I believe there are four critical measurement factors."

"What if we don't like the criteria they come up with?"

"Wayne." I look at him with concern in my eyes. "You have people on Walt's team. They're coming up with the criteria together. I think it's in your best interest to pay more attention to what these teams are doing, not to mention moving your own team along. If you don't get involved on the front end, you may find yourself a victim of someone else's decisions. And I'll hold you accountable for working within whatever system these teams come up with."

"What's that supposed to mean?"

"Think about it, Wayne." I stand up to leave. "Either you're part of the solution, or you're part of the problem. And I don't honestly know how you're going to get people to rave about these new systems when you have nothing positive to say about them yourself."

"What about the system Melissa's coming up with?" Wayne asks. "Can you tell me how that's going to work?"

"Why don't you ask Melissa or Rock?" I reply. "They'll fill you in."

Wayne sits in silence as I get up and leave his office. Only his scowl speaks. It tells me that I have a dangerous obstacle in my way - a clogged artery in the heart of the organization. How unfortunate for people to have to work for this man. No wonder they're gasping for air. And how unfortunate for me. If the medicine doesn't work,

I'm going to have to perform a bypass. The life of TYPCO is at stake.

CHAPTER 19

A s I head back to my office, I see Mark coming out of Bill's office.

"Hold on," I say. "Do you have a few minutes."

"Sure," Mark replies. "What do you need?"

"Well, I need to speak with you and Bill," I respond, leading Mark back into Bill's office and closing the door. Mark and I both sit down.

"Tell me how your teams are coming along," I inquire, looking first at Bill.

"It's real positive," Bill replies. "In fact, I'm starting to see some of our people actually wake up from the dead."

"Why do you say that?"

"Well, a lot of the people in Accounting and M.I.S. are conditioned to work *within* the system, not to *change* the system. This is a whole new experience for them. It's really getting people's attention."

"What kind of changes are you looking at?" I probe.

"The first thing we're trying to do is free ourselves up to spend more time working with Wayne and his production managers," Bill explains. "Right now, Wayne cannot be held accountable for a lot of things because he doesn't have access to certain information. And the only way we can develop information systems to support Wayne is if we declutter our own lives."

"What kinds of changes are you considering?"

"One happens to be our monthly closings," Bill explains. "Right now, we spend about one week per month on closing. That's a lot of time for a report that could easily be compiled quarterly."

"What about Wesley up at Corporate?" I ask. "Have you forgotten about him?"

"On the contrary. Wesley only needs certain specific information each month. He does not need a complete closing. We can still give Wesley what he needs without going through the complete process of closing. In fact, I'm willing to bet that the new reporting system will be even better for Wesley."

"Why do you say that?" I ask.

"Because I've already run it by him," Bill says. "And he likes the idea."

"So by going to a quarterly closing from a monthly one, we save eight weeks a year of accounting work?" I question.

"Not quite," Bill replies. "But we save a lot of valuable time, and we still generate the information we need at month end to track our performance."

"Wow!" I respond. "That's great!"

"And that will give us time to concentrate on more important things - like developing better tracking and information systems for production managers, and training people on things like budgeting and accounting."

"What kinds of systems are you looking to provide Wayne?" I ask.

"Standardized costing, budgeting, variance analysis, monthly P & L statements, cost of inventory data, operational expense, throughput dollars, all kinds of data. It's like your friend Jordan said - without information, people are quick to shift responsibility to those who have it. We've got to set things up out in the plant so that the producers know what the score is."

"And you feel that Wayne has been shifting responsibility to people outside of his control?" I ask.

Bill and Mark both turn and look at each other.

"You haven't observed this?" Mark asks.

"Maybe I have," I admit. "But apparently I haven't paid much attention to it. I suppose I owe you guys an apology for that."

"No apology necessary, Jack," Bill says. "Let's just solve the problem."

"And your solution is?"

"First, we have to put accountability where it belongs," Bill suggests. "Then we have to train people on how to meet their obligations."

"So the first step is to give Wayne a system that holds him accountable for his performance in dollars and cents terms?" I ask.

"That's right," Mark confirms. "But it isn't just Wayne. The reason I'm here is because I need the same kind of system for tracking our raw materials inventory."

"Wait a minute. I thought Bill just said that cost of inventories was one of the measurements he was going to develop for Wayne?"

"That's the cost of work-in-process inventory," Bill explains. "Mark is asking for the cost of raw materials inventory."

"And Nancy is asking for the cost of finished goods inventory," Mark adds.

"Why is that important to Nancy?" I ask.

They again turn and look at each other.

"You should probably talk to Nancy about that," Bill suggests. "As I understand it, she has quite a proposal for you."

"As do I," Mark interjects. "It has to do with some reengineering."

"Do you want to propose it now?"

Mark pauses for a moment and looks over at Bill.

"I suppose now is as good a time as any," he finally replies.

"Besides, Bill's been giving me some valuable advice on this."

"Good. I'm glad to hear that you two are working together."

"Without going into all the specifics, I'm proposing that we tie the whole procurement process together under my leadership," Mark explains. "This will include ordering materials, receiving materials, inspecting the materials and authorizing payment for the materials. We'll set it up like an internal vendor. I'll be responsible for making sure that our people have what they need when they need it. I'll also be accountable for making sure that our external vendors meet our quality standards. On top of that, I'll be accountable for managing the cost of our raw material inventory. Right now, I believe these costs are far too high."

"I see," I say quietly. This is the most initiative I've seen in Mark in years. "So you'd be taking over responsibility for Receiving, Incoming Quality Control, and Accounts Payable."

"That's right."

"And who would you report to?"

"My first choice would be you. No offense, Bill."

Bill laughs. "None taken."

"Well, that sure cuts across certain traditional lines, doesn't it?" I quip, thinking of Jordan's silos.

"There's no doubt about that," Bill confirms. "But look at what it can do for us? It breaks down walls. It declutters Accounts Payable. We can probably begin authorizing the payment of bills by simply matching what comes in the door with a purchase order. We won't even need invoices. That cuts the paperwork. It saves us time. And it saves us money."

"And it puts more pressure on our vendors," I add. "You two have given this a lot of thought, haven't you?"

"We've been working on it for three weeks now," Mark says. "Ever since that workshop."

"So you found the workshop helpful?" I ask.

"I think it's one of the smartest moves we've made in a long time," Bill replies. "If it were up to me, I'd do it every year."

"I agree," Mark adds. "I've heard nothing but positive things about it. It really got people thinking."

"Do me a favor then, will you?" I say.

"Sure, what's that?"

"Tell Rock what you just told me about the workshop. You know, it was his idea."

They both nod in agreement. These two are committed. I don't need any survey to tell me that.

"Well, how do you suppose Wayne will feel about giving up his jurisdiction over Receiving?" I ask.

"We figure that's where you come in," Bill says. "We may need a little help on this with Wayne and Roger. They're both going to have to give up some of their turf."

"And you don't mind giving up Accounts Payable, Bill?" I ask.

"Not under the circumstances," he replies. "It's the right thing to do, and Mark is the right guy to handle it. Besides, our new computer system handles all of the paperwork. All Mark's doing is authorizing payment for raw materials and plant supplies. We'll still cut the checks."

They both look at me with passion in their eyes.

"Well, I like the idea," I reply. "It cuts through some of our bureaucracy and puts acccountability where it belongs."

"That's what reengineering is all about, isn't it?" Mark says.

"Alright, then, here's what I want you two to do. I want you to put together an action plan on how you will go about implementing this new arrangement. Make sure you include new reporting relationships, new job responsibilities, and a timetable. Once I've had a chance to review your plan, we'll meet with the people involved and give them a presentation. If that goes well, I'll put the proposal in front of Corporate and ask for their endorsement. Until then, keep this to yourselves. I don't want it to scare anyone."

By the looks on their faces, they're ready to meet now.

"How soon can we meet?" Mark asks.

"As soon as your plan is finished."

"It's right here," Mark says, patting his notebook. "All I have to do is make copies."

"Then let's plan on next Wednesday at 8:00am," I reply. "I still need to meet with Wayne and Roger, and I want to find out how everyone else is coming on their proposals."

"Thanks, Jack," they both chime in.

"This is really going to make a difference," Mark adds.

It already has, I think to myself. It already has.

CHAPTER 20

Rather than return to my office, I now head towards Nancy's office, I wonder what Mark and Bill meant by suggesting that I meet with her. Why would our Customer Service Manager want information on the cost of finished goods inventory? Is this going to be another one of those break-down-the-walls ideas like Mark's?

My intuition is correct. Nancy's also been thinking big.

"So you want to take over the entire order fulfillment process?" I ask, looking at a sketch of her proposed organization chart. "And you're calling it Order Processing?"

"That's right," Nancy says confidently. "It's in our customers' best interest."

"Why do you say that?" I ask.

"Because without some control over the Scheduling and Shipping functions, there is little we can do in Customer Service to get our customers to rave about us," she explains. "We can *appease* them, but we can't really *please* them."

"Explain to me what you mean."

"Gladly," she continues. "Everyday, the phones ring continuously with questions about orders, shipments, special requests, overnight deliveries, changes, errors - you name it. But we're stuck in the middle. We always have to track down people in Scheduling and Production and Shipping to figure out what's going on. Meanwhile, our customers have to wait. The system is fragmented. It's slow. We're not working together."

So by merging Scheduling and Shipping and Customer Service, you believe we can manage the entire order fulfillment process in a way that better serves our external customers?"

"Without a doubt," Nancy replies. "Ultimately, our customer service reps and our schedulers will become interchangeable. And our shipping clerks will become much more engaged in customer affairs. We'll monitor the whole production process from order in the door to shipment out the door. Everyone involved in the process will be accountable to the same person."

"Have you run this idea by anyone else?" I probe.

"Only Mark and Bill and Jim, outside of our order fulfillment team," she answers. "In fact, they helped me come up with it."

"Jim?" I question.

"Yeah, you should talk to him. I think he wants to do something similar with Engineering."

Now, that really surprises me. Jim normally keeps to himself.

"Actually, it was your friend Jordan that got us thinking," Nancy says. "After the workshop, a bunch of us went into the lounge to pick his brain. Some people were there until after 10:00pm. It's too bad you couldn't join us. It was really interesting."

"And Jim stayed?"

"Yeah, he was still there when I left. He and Jordan seemed to hit it off really well."

"I wish I could've stayed," I reply earnestly. "But I promised my son I'd be at his basketball game."

"Well, I can understand that," Nancy says. "I have two kids of my own."

"Besides, my presence might have inhibited people."

Nancy stares at me.

"Do you really think you inhibit people?" she finally asks.

"I try not to," I answer. "But I know I do."

"I suppose that's true," Nancy admits with a sigh. "You do tend to scare some people."

"Can I ask you something, Nancy?"

"Sure. Go ahead."

"What would you do differently if you were me to get people to open up more and tell me what's on their minds?"

"I would do just what you're doing now," she replies, without hesitation. "I would spend more time getting to know people and letting them get to know you. I would get out and ask people for their opinions and listen to what they have to say - without judgement. If you ask me, the most proactive employee suggestion program in the world is doing what you're doing right now."

"But don't you think a lot of people simply fear me because I'm the boss?"

"I'm sure a lot of people make generalizations like that," she replies. "But if you ask me, it isn't the position that matters. It's the person in the position that makes the difference. Remember, I'm a boss, too."

Nancy is absolutely right. There is a lot I can do to get people to open up to me. I simply have to stop using my title as an excuse to explain why people don't level with me. It has little to do with my position. It's how I manage myself.

"Thanks, Nancy," I reply. "I appreciate your honesty."

"So what do you think of my proposal, anyway?" she probes.

"I think you're right on track," I answer. "The question is, how do we get there from here?"

"Well, Bill and Mark and Jim are already on board," Nancy explains. "Now comes the tough part. I still have to talk to Steve about it because of our reporting relationship. And then I have to talk to Wayne. I don't think he's going to like the idea of me taking over Scheduling and Shipping."

"Not to mention his giving up Receiving to Mark," I add.

"Does he know about that yet?" Nancy asks.

"Not yet," I reply. "And I've asked Mark and Bill to keep a lid on it until I talk to Wayne and Roger and Wesley."

"So you're going to support Mark on his proposal?" Nancy probes.

"It looks that way," I confirm. "I still need to see the action plan and get Corporate's endorsement, but I think the idea is right on target."

"That's great!" Nancy smiles. "I'm glad to hear that."

"Let's get back to your proposal," I say. "How do you suppose Steve will react to it?"

"That's a good question, Jack," she sighs. "I suspect he won't like it very much."

"Why do you say that?"

"Because it will mean that he has more responsibility outside of selling," she explains. "Under my proposal, he's going to have to pay more attention to fulfilling orders, not just taking them. It's an attempt to put selling and service on an equal plain."

"And you're concerned that Steve isn't interested in anything but selling?"

Nancy's expression answers my question.

"What if you reported directly to me?" I ask.

Nancy smiles.

"I've thought about that," she says. "As I see it, we have two options. One is to keep Sales and Order Processing under one heading and coordinate the activity - perhaps through small teams assigned to specific accounts. This benefits our external customers by giving them one contact - or team - to work with. It also gives our people more opportunity to develop cross-functionally." She pauses. "This means that I would continue to report to Steve - even with my broadened responsibilities - and that together we would be accountable for the whole process."

"And the other option is to report directly to me?" I probe.

"Yes. The other option is to set up Order Processing under it's own heading. This would mean that I report directly to you."

"What do you see as the advantages to this option?" I ask.

"First of all, it's clean," she explains. "It frees up Sales to go out and sell, which is all Steve really cares about. Second, it creates a flatter organizational structure. By reporting directly to you, rather than to Steve, I believe I can accomplish a lot more in terms of customer service, and you can be kept better informed."

I pause and think of Jordan.

"Let's look at it the other way around," I continue. "What are the adverse consequences to each option?"

"Well, I suppose the disadvantage to reporting to Steve would be that he's now accountable for Order Processing, as well as Sales."

"And you see this as a problem?"

"In my opinion, Steve is only interested in selling and wining and dining customers. He's not interested in anything that goes beyond that - including Management."

"So do you think Steve is in the wrong place?"

Nancy pauses, confirming my suspicions.

"I think we were all better off when Steve was just out selling. Ever since he became Sales Manager, the morale in my department and the morale among the Sales Reps has gone downhill - not to mention the negative feedback I get from some of his accounts."

"So the disadvantages to structuring this activity under Steve has more to do with Steve's performance as a manager," I clarify.

"That's my opinion," Nancy replies.

"What do you see as the disadvantages to your reporting to me?" I ask.

"My biggest concern with this option would be having Steve

out selling work that we can't schedule and ship under the terms he's promising customers. This would destine us to fail." She pauses. "It might also interfere with our setting up cross-functional account teams."

"It sounds like a lot revolves around the commitment we get from Steve." I pause. "So tell me, Nancy, what is your recommendation?"

Nancy sighs.

"Well, this has been a struggle for me," she explains. "Given these options, I guess the right thing to do is to put Sales and Order Processing together under one heading. This assures that we're not making promises to customers we cannot keep. It interconnects the various tasks and puts more emphasis on the whole process of serving our customers." She pauses. "My problem is with Steve."

"I'm with you."

"I just don't see how we'll ever get him to take this whole process seriously," she says. "He has a one-track mind."

"Tell me about your relationship with the Sales Reps, Nancy?"

"From my perspective, it's very positive," she replies. "We work together very well."

"Have you ever considered a position in Sales?" I fish, wondering if Nancy might be a potential replacement for Steve.

"Actually, that's where I started a long time ago," she responds.

"So how did you end up in Customer Service?" I probe.

"I didn't want to travel anymore. I needed a change."

"I see. And what about Scheduling? Have you ever worked in Scheduling?"

"No. I'm afraid not," she admits. "But I understand our system."

"I'll tell you what, Nancy. I think your proposal has excellent

potential. In fact, I think it could help us resolve several problems."
I stand up to leave. "Here's what I want you to do. I want you to
detail your proposal in the form of a complete business plan and
prepare to present it at our staff meeting next Wednesday. Be sure
to show who would do what, and how you would get people to buy
into it."

"What about Wayne and Steve?"

"Just prepare your plan. I'll talk to Wayne and Steve."

"Thanks, Jack." Nancy looks at me with new life in her eyes.
"You won't be disappointed."

You're right, Nancy, I think to myself. It's this kind of vision
and initiative I've been needing all along.

CHAPTER 21

A s I leave Nancy's office, I decide to pay Roger a visit. As
our Quality Assurance Manager, Roger is about to discover
some radical changes are in the making, and I don't think he knows
anything about them. It's too bad. Roger is a very talented
individual with immense potential. The problem is, he's reluctant to
take any risks. While Melissa, Bill, Mark and Nancy are beginning
to make bold, proactive proposals aimed at shaking things up,
Roger remains hesitant. I'm not really sure why.

When I arrive at Roger's office, I find it empty. Good, I think
to myself. It's nice to find someone in the organization who isn't
sitting behind a desk. I decide to track him down.

I find Roger in the Receiving Department, looking over a
batch of raw materials. He's standing next to some other guy.

"What's going on?" I ask.

"Well, it looks like we've got another bad shipment of
inserts," Roger says.

"What's wrong with them?" I continue.

"They've got grease on them," he explains, handing me an
insert. "Take a look."

"How did you discover this?" I ask.

"Rick found them," Roger answers, nodding to the young
man standing next to him. "Rick does our incoming quality
inspection."

"Who's the vendor?" I ask.

"Inserts Unlimited," Roger says. "They're always messing this order up."

"Then why do we continue to do business with them?"

Roger and Rick look at each other.

"It's a long story," Roger says. "I assumed you knew."

"I don't know anything about it," I counter. "What do you say we take a little walk, Roger. I need to talk to you about something else, anyway."

"Alright," he says, tossing a few inserts back into the bin. "Rick, I'll have to get back to you on these. Just tag the whole batch for now."

"What should I tell Wayne?" Rick asks.

"Tell him that these inserts are not to be used," Roger shouts, as we walk away. "If he has a problem with that, tell him to see me."

Roger shakes his head.

"So what's going on?" I ask.

"Can we go outside and sit down?" Roger asks. "I need a smoke."

"Sure," I reply, turning toward the door.

Not far from the Receiving docks, there is a small picnic area for the employees. The place is deserted. Roger and I walk over and sit down at a table. It's a fresh spring day and the flowers are just beginning to blossom. Roger pulls a cigarette from his shirt pocket and lights up.

"So what's going on with Inserts Unlimited?" I repeat.

"They're making a mockery out of our audits," Roger replies, taking a long drag from his cigarette. "They think they're invincible."

"So why are we doing business with them?"

"Two reasons," Roger explains, blowing smoke through his

nose. "First, we haven't found anyone else who can supply us with the inserts at the price we get." Roger hesitates.

"And the second reason?" I prompt.

"Second, and probably more important, Wayne insists that we use them. Apparently, he's in real tight with the owner. I thought you knew this."

"I didn't know anything about it!" I rebut. "How hard have we looked for other vendors?"

"Not very hard," Roger admits. "No one wants to cross Wayne. And a lot of people think you're in on this, too."

"What about Mark?" I ask. "Does Mark know about the quality problems we're having with Inserts Unlimited?"

"We've discussed it. But I don't think he knows the full story."

"Why not?"

"You'd have to ask Mark that," Roger responds. "But if you ask me, it probably has something to do with certain people catching hell every time they say anything."

"Like who?" I ask.

"Like Rick, for one. And Fred in Receiving."

"Rick handles incoming quality inspection, right?"

"That's right. And Fred handles Receiving." Roger takes another long drag from his cigarette. "And if either one of them rocks the boat too much, Wayne jumps all over them."

"But Rick reports to you," I say.

"That doesn't matter. Wayne gives everyone a hard time."

"So how does Mark know if the materials we're buying are acceptable or not?"

"We give him a report," Roger replies.

"So his feedback on the quality of our raw materials goes through you?"

"That's right," Roger confirms, looking to the sky and

releasing a cloud of smoke. "We check the goods and send him a copy of our report."

"Let me ask you something, Roger," I continue. "What if Rick and Fred both reported directly to Mark? Wouldn't that be putting accountability where it belongs?"

"I never really thought about it like that," he replies, flicking an ash from his cigarette.

"Well, think about it," I explain. "It would put accountability for all incoming materials under one heading. Mark's team would be responsible for ordering, receiving and inspecting all incoming materials. In fact, Rick and Fred could probably learn each other's jobs and cover for one another."

"You'd have to get the union to support that," Roger states.

"That's true," I admit. "But doesn't it make sense?"

"What about vendor audits?" he asks. "Who would conduct the audits?"

"I imagine we'd have a team perform the audits, just like we do now," I explain. "Maybe we could even expand the team to include people like Rick and Fred?"

"Under whose jurisdiction?" he proceeds, taking another drag off his Camel.

"Well, if we put Mark in charge of Receiving and Incoming QA, I trust he would be responsible for overseeing the vendor audits."

"What about me?" Roger asks quietly, flicking his cigarette.

"First of all, you would remain a valuable member of our vendor audit team. You and Mark would work collaboratively on vendor certifications."

"It sounds like you've been giving this a lot of thought," Roger says. "Can I ask where this leaves me?"

"You're right, Roger. I have been giving this a lot of thought. And, if you ask me, we've got to do a better job putting accountability where it belongs."

"And you think that by putting Mark in charge of Incoming QA, we'll see an improvement in the quality of our materials?"

"I would expect at least that," I explain. "You see, Mark would also be responsible for authorizing payment for all incoming materials. If the quality isn't acceptable, he won't pay for the goods. He'll just ship them back."

"What about Wayne?" Roger asks. "He'll go ballistic if Mark turns against Inserts Unlimited. And he'll never give up Fred."

"That's another issue," I reply. "In fact, that's what I originally wanted to talk to you about."

Roger looks at me cautiously.

"Go on," he urges, taking another drag from his cigarette.

"I've been rethinking a lot of things lately," I continue. "And, quite honestly, I don't know how much longer Wayne will be working here."

Roger looks stunned.

"What do you mean by that?" he asks.

"Well, Wayne has been given a very clear directive. He's either going to join us in our efforts to revitalize this company, or he's going to have to find someplace else to work. It's as simple as that."

"Wow," Roger sighs. "I never expected to hear this from you."

"First, let me insist that you keep our little chat to yourself for right now," I state firmly. "You're the only person in this company, aside from me, who knows anything about this."

"So why are you telling me?" Roger asks.

I pause and look directly at Roger.

"Because I'm considering you as a possible candidate for Wayne's replacement."

Again, Roger looks stunned.

"Geez, Jack. This conversation has gone from one where I thought I was getting fired to one where I think I'm getting promoted. What's going on?"

"Think about it, Roger," I continue quietly. "We're making a solid commitment to our principles. And we're looking for ways to reinforce this commitment. Wayne is getting in the way. I've talked to him on several occasions. I've offered him my support. The fact remains. He's not willing to change. You, on the other hand, have a great deal of potential here. You've got excellent credentials, and you understand our operation as well as anyone. You get along well with the people on the floor, and I know you aren't going to let anything but quality go out the door."

"What about my role as Q.A. Manager?" he questions. "Who would take over for me?"

"I was going to ask you that," I reply. "But as I see it, the role of the Q.A. Manager has to change. A lot of what you do now has to be shifted to other areas. I'm looking for a structure that cuts through all the bureaucratic nonsense and puts accountability where it belongs."

"So if I took over as Plant Manager, are you saying I would still have some Q.A. responsibilities?"

"Not Q.A., but Q.C.. You'd have all in-process quality control responsibilities - like you do now."

Roger leans forward and takes a long drag from his cigarette.

"What about Q.A.?"

"Quality Assurance would become more of a *visionary* function, not a *visual* function," I explain. "I'd like to see Q.A. concentrate on designing quality into our future, not on inspecting our day-to-day affairs."

"Does that mean you'd split the lab?" he probes.

"I don't know. I suppose the lab could be split. Some of it might be aligned under the Plant Manager, along with Quality

Control. The rest of it could report to Product Development."

"And incoming quality inspections would go to Mark?"

"That's the idea," I reply. "Along with Receiving."

"What about Scheduling and Shipping?" he probes. "Don't those functions currently report to Wayne?"

"They do now," I respond. "But that's causing us problems, too. We've got months' worth of finished goods inventory jammed into our warehouses, and we're scheduling the plant for *our* reasons, not the customers. I'm thinking about aligning them all under Customer Service."

"Under Steve?" Mark looks surprised.

"No. Under Customer Service," I state clearly.

He looks puzzled. Suddenly, a light goes on.

"I see," he says. "I take it there are some changes coming in Customer Service and Sales?"

"You'll keep this to yourself, I trust?"

"You have my word," Roger promises.

"Yes," I confirm. "There are a number of changes coming."

"What about things like getting standard operating procedures written. Who will be responsible for that?"

"As far as I'm concerned, it's every manager's responsibility to see that S.O.P.'s are written in their work areas," I respond. "Again, we have to put accountability where it belongs."

"I suppose you're right," he says. "How about corrective action plans to customers? Who do you see handling that."

"Sounds like something Sales, Q.A. and Customer Service will have to coordinate with the plant. Personally, I'd like to see whoever made the error write the corrective action plan."

"What about our ISO 9000 initiative? Who's going to drive that?"

"I'd like to set up a cross-functional team of people involving every department in the company to handle that," I explain. "This will give the people some ownership for writing S.O.P.'s. Each representative of the team will be responsible for forming and leading small action teams to develop S.O.P.'s for every process we have."

"These action teams will include users of the process?"

"Exactly," I confirm. "We'll get the users of the process to write the actual SOP's and the department heads will be responsible for following through."

"I think that's a great idea," Roger admits. "The people in the plant are always complaining about the procedures that the quality technicians write. This will give them ownership for doing it themselves."

"They'll also be responsible for conducting the training once the S.O.P.'s are written," I add. "They'll manage the whole process from start to finish."

"I like it," Roger smiles, taking a last puff of his Camel and snubbing it out in a tin ashtray. "It inspires people to think, and it gets them a lot more involved in our on-going improvement process."

"So what do you think of all this?"

"Well, you sure scared the hell out of me at first," Roger sighs. "But, I have to admit. It makes a lot of sense."

I think back to something Jordan had said. 'Show people the value in the change, and they may surprise you.'

"So do you have any interest in being considered for Plant Manager?"

"I'm not so sure I'm ready for that," Roger admits. "To be perfectly honest, I think I'm better suited for the Q.A. role."

"Well, I didn't expect an immediate answer," I assure him. "I just wanted to present it to you as an option."

"Can you tell me more about the Q.A. option?"

"Sure," I reply. "But before we get into that, let me just say this. First, I want you to know that I value your work here. I wouldn't consider you for either position if I didn't. Second, I think you have a great deal of potential. Choosing either of these options sure won't hurt your career any. Third, I don't think Wayne does you any good at all."

Roger looks surprised.

"What do you mean by that?"

"I think you listen to him too much," I reply. "I think you let him get in your way."

"Can I explain something?" Roger interjects.

"Sure, go ahead."

"The only reason I back off from Wayne is because everyone around here considers him untouchable. They consider him an extension of you. Believe me, the news of Wayne's departure will shock people."

"Will it be positive or negative?"

"Come on, Jack," Roger says. "Wayne's departure will be the single most powerful way possible for you to demonstrate your commitment to our mission and guiding principles. In fact, I still can't believe what I'm hearing."

"I had no idea that things on the floor were that bad," I say quietly. "Talk about an extreme case of Perception Warp."

"What?" Roger asks.

"Nothing," I reply. "I was just thinking aloud.

"So who else are you considering for the Plant Manager role?"

"To tell you the truth, I haven't really given it much thought," I explain. "You're the first person to come to mind."

"I appreciate your vote of confidence, Jack. So tell me more about the new Q.A. role."

"As I see it, this role would be more like that of an internal consultant representing our outside customers and linking

Engineering to Production," I explain. "You would report directly to me and maintain a staff of no more than one person."

"What would I be responsible for?"

"You would lead the ISO 9000 quality team I mentioned. You would participate in internal and external quality audits. You would work closely with Engineering, Sales and Customer Service on quality assurance issues. You would design and offer training classes. And you would work closely with the new Plant Manager and Q.C. Manager on quality control issues. Rest assured, you'll be plenty busy."

"Do you see the new Q.A. role as being a long term role?"

"That I don't honestly know. But I'll tell you what. We're going to start building this company around our winners. We may end up with an unusual looking organizational chart, but it won't be bureaucratic. And it won't be slow. And it won't be fragmented like it's been in the past. We're going to feed our go-getters with opportunity, and I'm going to pull any weeds that get in the way."

Roger smiles.

"I don't really know what to say, Jack. I suppose I should start by saying thanks for sharing this with me. I'm flattered that you trust me enough to open up like this, and I'm honored to be considered for Plant Manager. I guess I had you all wrong. I always assumed you and Wayne were one in the same."

"Let's be careful about what we assume, Roger," I reply, hopping up from the picnic table. "It's likely to get us both in trouble."

PART VI

Plug Yourself In

CHAPTER 22

By the time I arrive back to my office, the whole morning has whizzed by. Yet, unlike most days, I feel like I've accomplished a week's worth of activity. Melissa's team is moving full speed ahead on creating and implementing a far more productive performance management system. Walt's team is coming up with a new system that allows our production personnel to evaluate the service of our people in Skilled Trades. Bill's team is initiating some incredible ideas on how to streamline our accounting and information systems. Mark is putting together a plan on how to reengineer our procurement process and reduce the cost of our raw materials inventory. And Nancy is drawing up a plan on how to merge Scheduling and Shipping with Customer Service. I can't wait to hear the presentations next week.

Then again. I can.

The first message I see on my desk is from Wayne. Beneath it, are messages from Jim, our Engineering Manager, Rock, Steve, Melissa and Jordan. I decide to try Jordan first. He left a number for a hotel in New York. The message says he'll be there for another hour. I pick up the phone and dial his room.

"So are you going to be out socializing until the late hours again tonight?" I ask.

"I never promised you an 8:00 to 5:00 workshop," he replies. "If you ask me, we often get more done in the lounge than we do in the classroom."

"Well, I appreciate you spending a little extra time with my staff," I state gratefully. "They're really fired up!"

"Good," the man replies. "I'm not surprised. You have some very talented people working for you and a lot of opportunity to make things better."

"I'm beginning to see that."

"Well, I just wanted to call to follow up," Jordan continues. "I'm particularly interested in some of the proposals I trust you've seen by now."

"As a matter of fact, my ears are still ringing. I don't know what you told these people, but they're thinking big."

"Good," the man says. "That's what you want your managers to do. I simply helped them initiate business plans of their own. And I focused them on process rather than function. Ultimately, this makes your job easier."

"I hope so," I reply. "As it stands right now, I'm facing some pretty difficult decisions."

"Does one of them have to do with your friend Wayne?"

"Yes, as a matter of fact. That's the one bothering me the most."

"Is your friendship more important to you than your integrity?" the man asks.

"What if it is?" I reply.

"Then you don't belong in a position of leadership," he says confidently. "And that's fine. But as a leader, you're accountable to all of the people you lead. You cannot gain their commitment without managing yourself in an objective, consistent, principle-based manner."

"And this includes pulling the weeds?"

"Yes, it does," Jordan explains. "You owe it to your people to give them an inspiring leader. If you discover a weed, you must take action. You must confront your fears." He pauses. "Just remember. You never want to treat anyone like a weed. Remember your principle about dignity. People are not to be plucked from the organization and tossed aside. Give them the time and security they need to find another place to grow. It's the least you can do for a friend."

"How soon do you think I should act on this?"

"I take it you haven't seen any change in Wayne's behavior during the past few months?"

"Not really," I reply. "He pretends to go along. But his assumptions about people haven't changed."

"Do you have someone in mind to replace him?"

"I'm considering Roger."

"Roger," Jordan repeats. "He's your Q.A. Manager, isn't he?"

"That's right," I confirm. "You're good with names."

"It makes a difference to people."

"Well, anyway. I just talked to Roger about taking over as Plant Manager. He's the only one who knows about Wayne's predicament."

"Does Roger want the job?"

"I'm not really sure," I reply. "I just suggested it to him this morning."

"I see." The man pauses.

"You sound hesitant."

"Have you considered any other candidates?" he asks.

"No. Not really."

"And you think Roger will step in and take the lead?"

"I certainly hope so," I reply. "He can't do any worse than Wayne."

There is a long pause.

"Listen to what you're saying, Jack."

"What do you mean?"

"It doesn't sound to me like you're certain that Roger is an effective leader." The man pauses. "Tell me, why did you offer the position to him?"

"Well, he's very intelligent and well-educated. He's knows our operation inside and out. He gets along well with most people. He works hard. He cares about quality." I pause. "I think he's the best person we have for the job."

"Yet, you've looked at no other candidates," Jordan adds.

"True, but I have a lot of confidence in Roger."

"Does he have confidence in himself?" Jordan asks.

I pause for a moment. Where are these questions coming from? What criteria is Jordan using in qualifying Roger for the job?

"Sometimes he lacks a little initiative," I reply. "But once Wayne is out of the way, I believe Roger will rise to the occasion."

"How well does he develop people?"

"I think he does a pretty good job."

"So he has a capable successor to take over for him as Q.A. Manager?"

"Actually, I plan to redefine that role," I explain.

"That doesn't answer my question. Roger didn't know anything about a change in his role before this morning. Has he been developing someone in his department to take over for him?"

"I don't really know."

"So what kind of a mentor are you giving the people in the plant?" he asks.

"Maybe I overlooked that as part of the criteria," I admit.

"Well, it's worth thinking about," Jordan explains. "Removing Wayne as Plant Manager won't be perceived as being very positive in the long run unless a real winner replaces him."

"But I've already discussed the position with Roger," I say, wishing I'd kept my mouth shut.

"May I make a suggestion?" Jordan interjects.

"Please do."

"When you're considering organizational changes of this magnitude, think these decisions through carefully. Reengineering a company your size must be orchestrated carefully. Every decision, especially people decisions, must be handled deliberately. Otherwise, you'll create chaos."

"But, if I'm convinced that this is the right thing to do, shouldn't I just jump on it?"

"Not if it's going to turn a positive action into a negative result," he cautions.

"So what would you suggest I do?"

"Let me first say that I commend you on getting out and listening to your people. I trust it has opened your eyes to some things?"

"Very much so," I reply.

"Now try doing the same thing for a longer period of time," the man says. "Plug yourself into the equation."

"I don't understand."

"Have you ever considered taking over for Wayne yourself?" Jordan asks. "At least, for a few months."

I laugh.

"No, not really."

"Well, consider it, Jack. You run a manufacturing company. Your survival depends upon your ability to produce quality products in an efficient, profitable manner, right?"

"That's right."

"And this requires that certain functions serve you so that you can serve others, right?"

"That's right," I respond.

He pauses. I can hear him fumbling around on the other end of the phone. "Do me a favor. Take out a piece of paper and a pen."

I grab a blank index card from my shirt pocket, a new habit

I've developed.

"Okay," I reply. "I'm ready."

"Now, draw a circle in the center of the paper and label it Plant."

"Done," I say, crossing the T.

"Alright, this represents your plant. It's accountable for turning raw materials into a product you can sell, right?"

"Right."

"Good," he continues. "Now write down everything this involves."

"You mean all the various functions?"

"That's right. Write them down."

I begin to write. The first thing I write down is Receive Orders. Next, I write down Schedule Production. This is followed by Order Raw Materials, Receive and Inspect In-coming Materials, Produce Quality Parts, Manage Inventories, Control Costs, Ship Quality Products and Make Money. When I finish writing, I read my list to Jordan.

PLANT

* Receive Orders
* Schedule Production
* Order Raw Materials
* Receive and Inspect
  In-coming Materials
* Produce Quality Parts
* Manage Inventories
* Control Costs
* Ship Quality Products
* Make Money

"Alright, now look carefully at your list and tell me what you see."

As I do this, I realize what Jordan is driving at. Mark's new role as Procurement Manager and Nancy's new role as Order Processing Manager fall under the plant. Rather than taking responsibilites away from Wayne, I should probably be adding responsibilities.

"So you're suggesting we hold the Plant Manager accountable for customer service?"

"Think about it, Jack. If you're a customer, wouldn't you prefer to talk to someone who can give you a direct answer?"

As Jordan says this, my first reaction is to resist the idea. After all, we've always assumed that Customer Service belongs in Sales. But the truth is, this isolates them from the plant. It puts them in the awkward position of always having to get back to people.

"Wouldn't this be giving the Plant Manager too much authority? I mean, we could pile up months of costly inventory."

"Are you telling me you wouldn't measure this?"

Jordan's probably right. I should be holding my Plant Manager accountable for more than just cranking out parts. That's what's causing us so many problems now. And if Bill could get us the information we need to manage the process intelligently, what would we need all these silos for? Besides, if I took over as Plant Manager for awhile, these functions would still report to me. I'd be right in the middle of it all.

"Maybe you're right," I say, looking at the card in front of me. "So, what about the other functions?"

"I'll come back to those," he replies. "The important thing to remember is that your Plant Manager must be held accountable for everything that goes into turning an order into a quality product. Right now, it sounds as if you have some of these functions reporting elsewhere."

"That's true," I confirm. "But that's also what we're in the process of changing. To begin with, we're going to bring Quality Control in under the Plant Manager. We're also planning to merge Receiving and In-coming Quality Inspection with Purchasing. And we're considering merging Scheduling and Shipping with Customer Service."

"Good," the man says. "It sounds like you've been listening to Mark and Nancy."

"Among others," I respond. "There's a lot of powerful thinking going on around here right now."

"I'm impressed," Jordan says quietly. "Now think about taking over as Plant Manager for six months and having Roger report directly to you."

"What good do you think that would do?" I ask reluctantly.

"You tell me," he replies. "Think about it."

"Well, I suppose it would give me a chance to find out for myself how well the plant's running," I reply. "It would also give me a better indication of who the responsible people are."

"There's two good reasons," the man says. "What else?"

"I suppose it would also give me a chance to evaluate the service I'm getting from the functions that serve the plant." I add.

"That's three good reasons. Anything else?" The man won't let up.

I pause for a moment.

"It would give me a chance to implement some of these changes myself," I continue. "And it would give me a chance to evaluate the results."

"Sounds productive. Anything else?"

I wonder what he's fishing for...? Aha!

"It would allow me to see what Roger can do without Wayne around."

"There you go," Jordan says, as if seeing something I failed to see. "And it would give you a chance to consider other candidates for Plant Manager."

"That's true. But, in either case, I'm sure Roger and I can easily absorb the loss of Wayne for six months. I'll bet Roger will love this idea."

"Let me just say this, Jack. Any time one of your key managers leaves the organization, try filling the role yourself for a while. You might be surprised by what you learn."

"That's a good point. I'm sure I'd learn a lot."

"And since the plant is the heart of your organization," Jordan adds. "It's sounds to me like an excellent place to start."

"What about Sales?" I interject. "You know, I plan to let my Sales Manager go, as well."

"I'm not surprised," Jordan replies. "Do you have a replacement in mind."

"Not really. I was considering Nancy."

The man is silent for a moment.

"Why?" he finally asks.

"Because she's done an excellent job for us in Customer Service, she gets along great with the Sales Reps and she has a background in Sales."

"That's a leap of faith," Jordan says softly. "So you consider her a sound mentor for your Sales Reps?"

Jordan's question catches me by surprise.

"I don't know," I respond. "Maybe not."

"Then why put her where she's destined to fail?"

I remain silent.

"Tell me something, Jack. What kind of mentor do you suppose your Sales Reps need?"

"Probably someone who can teach them more about what they're selling."

"And what exactly is that?"

I think back to something Jim said in one of our meetings.

"We're selling our engineering and manufacturing capability," I say quietly. "Along with outstanding service."

"That's right," comes the reply. "Now, is Nancy an engineer?"

Jordan knows the answer.

"No."

"So what is she going to be able to offer the Sales Reps other than a pleasant personality and a strong work ethic?"

"I guess you're right. In our business, Nancy probably belongs in a more administrative function."

"Like Order Processing?"

"Yeah, I know she can handle that."

Again, there is a long pause.

"Has she ever scheduled any production before?"

Geez, this guy won't let up. What's he got against Nancy."

"No, I don't think so," I respond.

"Then what makes you think she can manage the Scheduling function?"

"Well, she wouldn't be doing the actual scheduling," I reply in Nancy's defense. "She'd simply oversee the activity."

Jordan is silent for a moment.

"I don't mean to be giving you such a hard time on this, Jack," he finally explains. "I just want to make sure you're considering the facts when you make management decisions of this magnitude. Your ultimate success will revolve around the people you surround yourself with. It sounds like Nancy has great potential. She has vision, and she shows initiative. She also has sales experience, and she gets along well with people. On the other hand, she's not an engineer and she has limited experience in scheduling a manufacturing operation." Jordan pauses. "You've got to take this one step at a time, or you're going to create chaos."

"In other words, if I stretch her responsibilities too far and too fast, I may be setting her up to fail at something she's clearly capable of doing in the long run?"

"Precisely. You've got to *enable* her before you can *empower* her."

Jordan's right. That's one of the biggest mistakes I tend to make. I overlook important facts when making people decisions. I act in haste.

"So what would you suggest I do?"

"Groom her for the position. Give her a mentor. Develop a plan. Set some goals. Give her the training and resources she needs to be successful at the job. Break it down into steps. She will appreciate that."

"In other words, don't just leap in."

"Don't get me wrong, Jack. I admire your enthusiasm and initiative. In fact, you're probably going to accomplish more in a year than some companies do in three years. Just don't let your emotions cloud your judgement."

"So who would you have Nancy report to?"

"Let's go back to your little diagram," he says. "Would you agree that, ultimately, you'd like to have all of these functions tied together?"

"Yeah, I think that's moving us in the right direction."

"Now, tell me more about what Roger is capable of?"

"Well, like I said before, he knows the plant as well as anyone. He understands Quality Control. He's worked with our vendors and customers."

"Has he ever scheduled production before?" Jordan interjects, as if knowing the answer.

"As a matter of fact, that's where he started with TYPCO."

Jordan doesn't say a word. A light goes on...

"So you think Roger might qualify as Nancy's mentor?"

"Think about it, Jack. You've already considered Roger for Plant Manager. And, as you've probably surmised, I have a problem with that at this point in time. But putting him in charge of a process like Production Control is a different story."

"What exactly do you mean by Production Control?" I ask.

"Production Control oversees everything from ordering raw materials to shipping finished goods out the door. It's your command and control center."

"Does that include Quality Control?"

"Absolutely - from raw materials to finished goods."

"So it includes Mark's new responsibilities, as well."

"That's right."

I stop and think for a moment. This would mean that Mark and Nancy both report to Roger. He would be responsible for merging the functions and cross-training the people. He could help Nancy understand more about Scheduling and Shipping, and he could help Mark understand more about Receiving and Quality Control. He would also be responsible for monitoring our entire manufacturing process, including inventories and machine downtime. Best of all, he would become a direct link between our plant and our customers.

"What about Quality Assurance?"

"Roger doesn't understand Q.A.," Jordan says bluntly.

"What do you mean?" I ask. "He's our Q.A. Manager."

"That's just what you call him," the man counters. "But he isn't doing anything more than control and inspection work."

Jordan's right. We renamed the function three years ago as part of our T.Q.M. initiative, but, in reality, nothing's really changed. Roger is a control person, not a visionary.

"So what do you think we should do about Q.A.?" I ask.

"Talk to Jim," the agent of change replies. "I think he can probably help you out."

I'm tempted to press Jordan for answers, but I know he'll make me work for them. Perhaps it's best to be patient and follow through on his advice.

"So Roger takes over as our Production Control Manager reporting directly to me. This means merging Mark, Nancy and Roger all together. They each have broadened responsibilities, but they also have a mentor to help them succeed. It eases them into their new roles with sensitivity and support."

"That's right."

"And Q.A. remains separate."

"That's right."

"And if I fill in as Plant Manager for awhile, I'll have a chance to implement and evaluate the whole system."

"Precisely. Just remember to break it down into steps.

"Why is that so important?" I ask. "I've always been told to make organizational changes in one bold sweep."

"So you think that when this is over, nothing else will change?"

"No," I reply. "I anticipate a lot of on-going change."

"In other words, change will become the norm, rather than the exception?"

"I suppose that's true," I mutter.

"And how do you want people to feel about change?"

"Ideally, I'd like them to look forward to it."

"Then, if these changes are likely to be perceived as being positive, why not introduce them diligently so that people don't get the wrong message? Let your people experience the positive side of change. Give them a chance to gain from it."

"In other words, if I introduce the changes too quickly, the positive could be perceived as negative."

"That's absolutely right. I'm not suggesting that you delay important decisions. I'm only suggesting that you plan your course of action rationally and deliberately. Otherwise, your haste will work against you."

I pause and look down at the drawing I have in front of me.

"So what about the other functions?" I ask. "Where do they go in relation to this circle?"

"Some of them go around the perimeter of your plant," Jordan answers. "And some of them don't belong in this picture at all."

"How do you figure?"

"Think of it like our solar system. Your plant is the Earth. This is where you live. Some of the functions revolve around your plant, just as the moon revolves around the Earth. Your plant, on the other hand, revolves around your customers, just as the Earth revolves around the sun. Remember, without the sun, we cannot survive here on Earth."

"That's a bizarre way to think of a company," I laugh. "So which functions revolve around the Earth, and which functions revolve around the sun?"

"Think about why each function exists, and you'll discover the answers," the man replies. "Every value-added function has a purpose."

"This certainly creates an odd-looking organizational chart."

"Who cares what it looks like," Jordan responds. "It's what it accomplishes that matters."

"Well, it definitely reinforces our first principle - think like the customer."

"It also gives you another reason to reengineer some of your processes," he adds. "It brings sunlight into your plant."

"It does more than that," I add.

"What do you mean?"

"It gives me another good reason to take over as Plant Manager for a few months. Right now, we don't think this way at all."

"This kind of change takes time, my friend, so you must be patient. Just remember, if you act too swiftly, positive actions can have negative results. Go for first downs, not touchdowns. Set goals your people can achieve and gain from. Concentrate on building momentum."

"I hear you," I confirm. "Thanks for the tip."

"Don't mention it."

I'm about to hang up the phone when Jordan plants one more seed.

"By the way," he says. "Are you aware that you missed a few items when you defined the responsibilities of the plant?"

"What do you mean?" I ask.

"Talk to Melissa and Jim," he says. "I'm sure you'll find it enlightening."

CHAPTER 23

As I hang up the phone, I see Melissa and Rock standing in the doorway.

"Can we talk to you?" Melissa asks.

"Sure. Come on in."

The two walk in and sit down in front of my desk.

"We've got a proposition for you," Melissa continues. "But you've got to hear us out before jumping to any conclusions."

"That's fair enough," I reply. "What's the deal?"

"We want to reopen our labor contract - or at least part of it."

"What are you after?" I ask suspiciously.

"We want to add a few new job classifications," Rock says.

"Now, hold on a minute," I interject. "You both know how I feel about adding more classifications. We've got enough fragmentation around here as it is."

"Wait a minute, Jack," Melissa interrupts. "You promised to hear us out before jumping to any conclusions."

"I know I did, but what good can come from adding more job classifications. We've got too many as it stands now."

"We agree with you," Rock says. "That's exactly why we want to add a few more."

I shake my head in defeat.

"Now you've completely lost me."

"Let me put it this way, Jack," Melissa explains. "Would you agree that we're limiting people the way we're set up right now?"

"I would definitely agree with that," I answer. "Our job classifications are far too narrow the way they're currently defined."

"So you would like to see them broadened?" Rock asks.

"That's what I've been saying now for the past three years, Rock."

"And I've heard you," the big man replies. "But I've got to sell it to the people."

"And the people are resisting the idea of our forcing them into broader classifications," Melissa adds. "They don't trust us."

"So you want to add more?" I question. "How is that going to solve the problem?"

"The classifications we want to add, Jack, are cross-functional classifications," Melissa explains. "They will serve to bridge certain classifications together."

"It ties in with our new performance management system and cross-functional training initiative," Rock adds. "This way, we can begin to give people some incentive to learn more than one job. It's one of the criteria we plan to measure in the review process."

"I take it these new classifications will pay more?" I probe.

"Yes, they will," Melissa answers. "But they should. If Jane Doe can handle multiple jobs, shouldn't she earn more than John Doe who can handle only one?"

"Good point."

"And think about the flexibility it will give us," Rock adds. "People will be able to cover for one another without all the hassles we currently run into."

"How do you think the people will feel about it?" I ask.

"Most of them will like it," Rock answers. "It creates an on-going learning opportunity for them."

"But I thought you just told me that people don't want broader classifications?"

"We said that people don't want to be *forced* into broader classifications," Rock explains. "This doesn't force them."

"It inspires them," Melissa adds. "It puts the decision in their hands. It gives them a choice."

"Leadership is like a piece of string," I say to myself. "Push it, and it piles up in front of you. Pull it, and it follows you anywhere."

"Excuse me," Melissa says.

"Nothing," I reply. "I was just thinking about something Jordan said. It's not important."

"I doubt that," Rock says. "It was Jordan who gave us the idea."

"How's that?"

"We asked him if he had any suggestions on how to inspire people to do more than one job," Melissa explains.

"And what did he say?" I ask curiously.

"He said to give them incentive," Rock replies. "Deal with the 'what's in it for me?' factor."

"He also said to make it their decision," Melissa adds. "This proposal covers both."

"So these new classifications will begin merging other classifications together?" I ask.

"That's right," Melissa replies. "Eventually, they may be the only classifications we have left."

"So you want to *increase* the number of job classifications to *reduce* the number of job classifications?" I mutter in disbelief. "That sounds like a Jordan idea."

"So what do you think?" Melissa asks.

"Well, I have to admit that it sounds a little backward, but it does have some merit."

"It's full of merit," Rock explains. "It gives people more opportunity and variety. It gives them a chance to learn new skills.

It gives them a chance to earn more money. And it gives them the right to decide their own futures."

"Not to mention what it can do for the company, Jack," Melissa adds. "It gives us a chance to develop more responsible people. It increases our flexibility. It enables us to be more efficient and productive. It gives us an opportunity to deal more effectively with absences and emergencies. And, in the long run, it streamlines a lot of the bureaucracy in our plant."

"You two have a pretty good pitch. I'll admit that." I lean back in my chair. "I'll tell you what. Put together a plan detailing exactly what you want to do and what you expect it to accomplish. Be sure to explain how you plan to keep the system in check, as well. The last thing we need around here is a group of high priced people who only make boxes. You can present it at our meeting next Wednesday. We'll make a decision from there."

"Does this mean that you're open to the idea?" Rock asks.

"Why wouldn't I be, Rock," I reply. "If it moves us in the direction we want to go, you'll have my support."

CHAPTER 24

"What can I do for you, Jim?" I ask, leaning my head into an office that looks like the aftermath of an earthquake.

Jim Duran is our Engineering Manager. He's been with TYPCO for about eight years now, and he's one of the key reasons we're still in business. When it comes to new product development and process engineering, Jim is a master of the science.

"Hi, Jack," he says. "Thanks for stopping by."

I walk into the office and sit down in front of his cluttered desk.

"I heard you wanted to see me."

The man spins around in his chair and grabs a set of sketches from his credenza. He then stands and walks around to my side of the desk.

"Yeah. I want to get your opinion on something," he responds. "It has to do with rethinking the way we're organized."

"Go on," I urge.

He refers me to the sketch in front of us. Jim likes to think in pictures.

"As you know, we currently have all of our engineering work grouped together under one heading. This includes Product Development, Process Engineering, Tooling, Robotics, and Maintenance of Specialty Equipment."

"Not to mention Corporate R & D," I add.

"That's right. But the way Jordan McKay was talking a few weeks ago, I don't think we're going about things right."

"What do you mean?" I ask, looking over at him.

"As ironic as this may sound," he says, "I think Engineering needs to be reengineered." He points to four distinct silos drawn on the paper. One silo is labeled Product Development. Another is labeled Process Engineering. A third silo is labeled Tooling. And the fourth silo is labeled Robotics and Specialty Maintenance. "Right now, we have all four of these functions reporting directly to me. Yet, if we look at each function's core purpose, it would appear that some of them belong in the plant."

"Like what?" I ask.

"Like everything except Product Development and Tooling Design."

"So everything relating to the manufacturing process should report to the plant manager?" I ask.

"That's how I see it." He turns and looks at me. "Think about it this way, Jack. Who would you say is Engineering's customer?"

"I guess that depends on what element of Engineering you're talking about." As I say this, I suddenly realize what Jim's driving at. Product Development and Tooling Design primarily serve our external customers. But Process Engineering, Tooling Repair and Specialty Maintenance actually serve the plant. So this is what Jordan meant when he said I had missed a few functions.

"That's exactly my point," Jim says. "If we're going to look at this from the customer's perspective, then we've got to put the accountability where it belongs."

"Maybe you're right. Maybe we do need to rethink the way we've organized our engineers and technicians."

"Which creates an interesting dilemna for me," Jim adds. "Hypothetically, I could be eliminating my own job."

Jim is probably the only person at TYPCO who would make

such a bold statement. The man no doubt knows he's good at what he does, and he doesn't fear the loss of his job the way most people do. Come to think of it, he probably has recruiters calling him every week.

"What makes you say that?" I ask.

The man walks back around his desk and sits down.

"If the Process Group reports to the Plant Manager, and if the Product Development Group reports to Sales, what do you need me for?"

"Wait a minute. Who said anything about the product development engineers reporting to Sales?"

"Think about it, Jack. Doesn't that make sense to you?" The man leans back in his chair, draws one hand up to his chin and stares at me.

For once in my life, I honestly don't know what to say. One of my key players is telling me to eliminate his job.

"Hold on a minute, Jim," I gasp. "Let's talk about this."

"That's why I called you. I want to talk about it."

I pick up a sample product off the corner of Jim's desk and begin to fiddle with it.

"So explain to me where you see yourself in all of this. I mean, you're a key player around here, Jim. I don't want to lose you."

"I'm not suggesting I leave the company, Jack." I breath a sigh of relief. "I'm only suggesting that we look at the situation objectively."

"So where do you think you belong?"

He ignores my question.

"Look, the more sophisticated our customers get, the more sophisticated our products get. And the more sophisticated our products get, the more sophisticated our processes get." The man leans forward, placing both elbows on his desk. "Jack, we don't have any choice. We sell solutions, not just products. If we're going to honestly get people to rave about us, we've got to better integrate Engineering into our selling and manufacturing processes. Right now, we're isolating our engineers. We're designing things that don't make any sense to our customers."

"Or cost too much to manufacture," I add.

"That's right. And it's like you said the other day, that's where our real competition lies - in poor designs and excessive costs."

Jim's right. We've built walls up around Engineering, just like we have in every other department. On paper, TYPCO looks like a field of silos. And it's crippling our organization. We spend more time pointing fingers at one another than we do delivering solutions to our outside customers.

"So where do you see yourself in all of this?" I repeat.

"To be quite honest, I'd like to get more involved in Sales," he says. "My real strengths lie in Product Development, not Process Engineering. And I think I can add greater value to the company by spending more time collaborating with our outside customers."

My mind races immediately to my problem with Steve. Is this just blind luck, or am I so narrow-minded that I never even considered Jim for a position in Sales?

"What would you suggest we do with Steve?"

Jim leans back and begins rocking in his chair.

"That's a question I've been thinking about for a long time, Jack. And with all due respect to Steve, he's not an engineer. He doesn't understand our manufacturing processes." The man sighs. "If you ask me, Steve's role in this organization is changing, and I don't see how Steve is going to keep up. The days of pampering customers over a game of golf or showering them with gifts are over. Our customers want results, not sweet talk."

Jim's right. Steve often gets us into trouble because he doesn't really understand what he's selling. He never spends any time in our plant, and when it comes to mechanical know-how, he's totally incompetent. It's like we have a car dealer trying to sell F-16's.

"Sorry to put you on the spot like that, Jim, but I have to let you in on a little secret."

I lean forward.

"I'm looking for a replacement for Steve."

Jim nods his head as if not surprised. He and I have talked about these problems in the past.

"Do you have anyone in mind for the job?"

"Not really. I'm still trying to figure out how to define the job.

"May I make a suggestion?"

"Absolutely," I say.

"Merge Sales and Product Development. The two belong together in this business. We'd have our engineers working cooperatively with our customers' engineers to jointly design products. It's what our customers want."

"What would you do with Customer Service?" I ask curiously.

"Personally, I'd stick them out in the plant with Scheduling and Shipping. That way our customers could get direct answers from someone who actually knows what's going on in Production. Right now, it's like playing cat and mouse trying to get answers - and the customer isn't raving about it."

"That's interesting," I say quietly.

"In fact, I'd put them in charge of monitoring our whole manufacturing system, including in-process and finished goods inventory. Right now, we don't have any real controls in place on either one."

"So they'd be more like a Production Control Department than a Customer Service Department," I smile.

"Call them anything you want, Jack. The point is, they'll

know more about what's going on in this place than anyone. And our customers want to talk to people who have answers."

I laugh. No wonder Jordan wanted me to talk to Jim.

"And if you want to take it one step further," he continues, "I'd put Mark out there, too. Right next to Nancy and her gang. Having him report to Bill never made any sense to me."

"Why would you do that?

"Same reason. Mark serves the plant. But I'd expand his role, too. I'd put him in charge of ordering, receiving, inspecting and monitoring all raw materials inventory, not just lining up vendors and placing orders. He'd oversee the whole process."

Jim's obviously in the loop.

"How do you suppose Wayne would react to all of this?" I ask.

"Personally, I don't think he'd like it. It eliminates too many of his excuses. But, like I said, I'm trying to be objective about this."

"So not doing it just because of Wayne's resistance could be costing us."

Jim nods his head.

"It could be doing more than that," he says softly. "It could be killing us."

"What about Pricing? Where would you put that?"

"I think pricing a new product has to be a joint decision between Product Engineering, Process Engineering, Production, Production Control and Accounting. But, in terms of responsibility, I'd put it under Sales and Product Development. It forces us to be accountable to the market when we design products."

"Makes a lot of sense, Jim," I say after a brief pause. "You've obviously given this a lot of thought."

He smiles. He knew I would understand.

"Let's talk about Process Engineering?" I continue. "Who

would you put in charge of that?"

"I'm glad you asked." Jim leans back in his chair and puts both of his hands behind his head. "Duane Campbell."

I could have guessed. Duane's a brilliant process engineer. Jim continues.

"To tell you the truth, Duane knows more about process engineering and specialty equipment than I do. And he's damn good with the people out on the production floor. He's a natural for the job."

"And you don't mind giving him up?"

"I'm not giving him up, Jack. We're all on the same team."

"Hmm. So Duane takes the process side and reports to the Plant Manager, and you take the Product Development people and head up Sales. The idea has a lot of merit."

Jim sits quietly and studies me. Suddenly, I have an idea.

"Tell me something, Jim. Do you think Duane has the potential to become a plant manager?"

Jim smiles.

"Yes and yes."

"What's the second yes for?"

"He wants it."

Blind luck just struck again. Why don't I see these things? The more I think about it, the more I realize that Duane has the capacity to become an outstanding plant manager. First, he understands nearly every piece of equipment we have in the plant. In fact, he could probably build half of them. Second, he has instinct. He knows what needs to be done. Third, he has drive. The man gets things done. And fourth, he can teach. We'd be giving our people an excellent mentor. Maybe these are some of the characterisics Jordan was looking at in challenging me on Roger.

"What would you do with Tooling?" I ask.

"Split it," he explains. "Tooling Design comes with me.

Tooling Repair reports to the plant."

As Jim says this, I can't help but think about the immense opportunity this presents for the plant. Right now, it's like pulling teeth to get a simple mold repair done. And the downtime is sucking money right off our bottom line. There's no accountability. Talk about creating an opportunity for a competitor to get the best of us.

"And the lab?"

"Same as Tooling. New product testing comes with me. On-going production testing and process control reports to the plant."

Again, this makes perfect sense. It places the accountability where it belongs and eliminates a lot of wasted time and fingerpointing.

"And Quality Assurance?"

Jim pauses.

"First, I think we have to define the difference between Q.A. and Q.C.. To my way of thinking, Quality Assurance should become more of an engineering function linking Product Development with Process Engineering and Production. And Quality Control, which is all we really do now, should monitor the quality of our products."

"So you think Q.C. should report to the Plant Manager?" I ask.

"Or the Production Control Manager," he clarifies. "But, in either case, Q.A. should become a separate function."

"Who would you put in charge of Q.A.?"

"I think we should consider Marjorie," he says without hesitation. "She's an excellent engineer and she has experience in both product and process design. She'd be great!"

"What about Roger?"

"Roger's better at Production and Quality Control. Besides, he's not an engineer. I don't think he really understands what Q.A.

is all about. If he did, we'd be doing it right now."

Jim hits the nail on the head. We don't have a genuine Q.A. process in place because the guy who's in charge of it doesn't know what it really means.

"Have you talked to anyone else about your ideas, Jim?" I ask.

"Only in theory," he replies. "But we do have a consensus in terms of the concept."

"Among who?" I ask.

"Among the engineers."

"And you don't think you'll have any trouble shifting the engineers into one area or another?"

"I said we have a consensus in concept, not in application," he rebuts.

"What do you mean?"

He pauses.

"Let me be blunt," he continues. "No one wants to report to Wayne."

"Geez, Jim. You're just full of good news today." I laugh.

"Seriously, Jack. This presents a real problem for some people."

"But in concept, they agree it makes sense?" I clarify.

"That's right. In fact, most of them view it as a real opportunity to develop themselves."

"How's that?"

"The way I presented it, a product engineer would have to start out working in Process Engineering. This gives them very useful insight into our manufacturing process. From there, they could either move into Product Development and Sales, or remain in Manufacturing. Right now, I have three engineers who would love to move into Sales, and they already have the process background. I have two more who might someday qualify, but they need more process experience. The rest of the engineers, including Duane, prefer to focus on process engineering. They like working in the plant. Actually, the numbers work out really well."

"How soon would you be ready to move on this?"

"We could implement this anytime. But there are two critical success factors. One is to figure out how to deal with Wayne. The other is to get the Sales Reps to buy into the idea. I don't want to scare anyone."

"How would you handle the Sales Reps?"

"First, I'd meet with all of them to explain the concept - just like I did with the engineers. Then I'd propose teaming them up with Product Engineers by accounts. This way they begin to learn more about the relationship between the two traditional functions."

"What about down the road?"

"I'd begin to circulate the conventional Sales Reps through an in-plant training program. I've already talked to Duane about it and he thinks the idea is great. We'd design the program together."

"So the Reps would have more exposure to our internal manufacturing processes."

"That's right. And Duane plans to do the same thing with the people in Maintenance and Tool Repair. Ultimately, they'll be able to fix anything in the plant."

As Jim says this, I think back to Melissa's and Rock's proposal to reopen the labor contract. They wanted to create a few cross-functional, high-powered classifications aimed at providing opportunities for continuous learning and cross-utilization.

"So by moving Duane into Production, we're creating an opportunity for our producers to improve their technical skills."

"That's right. Our mechanics will learn more about process engineering and tooling. Our tooling people will learn more about our operating processes and maintenance. Our production people will learn more about preventive maintenance, machine care and tooling. It's like everyone is in an apprenticeship program - not just our skilled trades people - and that includes our sales reps."

"I'm impressed, Jim. I think you've come up with a real blockbuster here."

"Actually, it's Jordan McKay who deserves the credit. If you ask me, he's the one who busted things loose around here."

"Why do you say that?" I ask.

"Because, in retrospect, I don't think we've been operating on all of our cylinders - and he opened our eyes to it."

I smile and think of Kathleen's gerbil - working real hard and getting nowhere.

"I can't disagree with that. Maybe it's time for a major tune-up."

CHAPTER 25

On my way out of Jim's office, I see Duane and Walt talking with Ben Johnson, one of our production managers. I decide to pay them a visit.

"What's the news?" I ask as I approach.

Duane speaks first.

"We're working up a proposal for you." he says.

"Good for you. Do you want to tell me about it?"

Walt speaks next.

"Well, we're still working out a lot of the details. But, to summarize, we're looking for a way to help our service mechanics improve their skills. As it stands now, we don't have any formal development program in place to help them keep up with the times. They're just maintaining the old equipment and relying on the process technicians to handle the more sophisticated machinery."

"Basically, they're just flying by the seat of their pants," Duane adds. "They don't really understand a lot of our new equipment."

So they're becoming obsolete along with some of our old equipment, I think to myself. Why am I not surprised?

"Go on," I probe.

"So we're looking for a way to accelerate their learning," Walt continues. "You know, kind of like an on-going apprenticeship program."

"Only more than that," Duane interjects. " What we're really looking for is something that ultimately develops our people into high powered service technicians."

"How is that different from what we have now?" I ask.

Ben jumps in.

"Right now, our production operators don't know anything about maintaining the machinery," he says. "They just focus on the output."

"And our maintenance people don't know anything about tooling," Walt adds. "They just concentrate on the machinery."

"Not to mention process engineering," Duane adds. "And robotics. And electronics. And quality assurance. Our people are isolated from one another. They don't have access to the big picture."

"So what exactly are you guys looking to do?" I ask.

"We want·to create a system that gives our people the opportunity to learn these skills and be rewarded for it."

"Can I ask how it works?" I probe curiously.

"Well, we're still in the developmental stages," Duane explains. "But basically it would work like a person climbing up a ladder." Duane grabs a notepad from a nearby table and sketches a ladder on it.

| LEVEL IV |
| LEVEL III |
| LEVEL II |
| LEVEL I |
| ENTRY |

"Each rung of the ladder would have a defined criteria or set of goals to be met. So if a service mechanic wanted to reach Level

IV, for example, he would have to pass a test proving that he is capable of doing that level work - and that would include a lot of cross-training."

"Who would develop the criteria and administer these tests?"

"A team of people representing Production, Process Engineering, Tooling, Q.A., Maintenance and Human Resources," Walt replies. "It would be kind of like an internal interviewing process."

"And if I fail to meet the criteria?" I ask.

"You stay within your current level and pay range until your next review," Walt says. "But at least you have a clear set of goals for advancement. And there is no pressure on you to move to the next level."

"So the criteria gets more difficult the higher up you go."

"Absolutely," Duane says. "In fact, at the higher levels, you'd have to attend college engineering and management classes. This is one of the factors that keeps the system in balance."

"So if a person doesn't want to advance to the next level?"

"Then they stay at the level they're at," Walt explains. "Not everyone in this place wants to become an engineer or production manager."

"But there's dignity associated with each level," Ben adds. "We're not creating these levels to suppress people. We're creating them to reward people who want to do more than they're doing now."

"So an electrician, for example, could choose to stay where he is, or he could work to meet a higher set of criteria to advance himself?"

"That's right," Ben replies. "And we have people who would do both."

"Would this also apply to our production operators?" I ask.

"That would be the logical next step," Duane says. "Once we

create a system for our mechanics and tooling people, we plan to set up the same kind of program for the production operators."

"This means that as a service mechanic learns new skills from a process engineer, quality engineer or tooling specialist, he can begin to pass more information and knowledge down the ladder," Walt adds. "He becomes a trainer, as well as a student."

"What makes you think the service mechanics are going to pass the knowledge on?" I rebut. "Isn't that one of the problems we have now?"

"One of the criteria to pass to the next level requires that you serve as a trainer to the lower levels," Duane counters. "You have no choice but to train others if you wish to advance yourself."

"Hmm. That's pretty good."

"And we'll also tie the new development program into our Service Feedback System," Walt explains. "To advance to the next level, you're going to have to do more than learn new skills and train people. You're also going to have to deliver outstanding service to your customers."

"So what you're really talking about is creating an upward learning opportunity for everyone in Maintenance, Tooling, Production and Process Engineering."

"That's right," Duane says. "We're giving people defined goals with very specific qualifying criteria, and we're supporting them with training, guidance and cross-functional exposure."

"And we're leaving the decision up to the people," Walt adds. "If they want to learn new skills and contribute more, they can do so."

"And they'll be rewarded for this?" I ask.

"That's where we are with it right now," Walt explains. "We've talked to Melissa about the reward system, and she says we have to reopen the labor contract to do so."

"Don't let that scare you," I reply. "Anything's possible."

"We were hoping you'd say that," Duane says with a smile. "That's why we're putting this proposal together."

"So, to summarize, you're talking about creating a formal development program for our people. The criteria will be clearly defined, controls will be developed to keep the system in check, the support will be in place for those who choose to advance themselves, and the reviews will *inspect* exactly what we *expect.*"

"Couldn't have said it better myself," Walt laughs. "So what do you think?"

"I think it's great! Sort of makes me wonder why we aren't doing it now."

"Well, that's the next hurdle," Walt says, returning to a serious tone. "Wayne's kind of giving us a hard time on this."

"Why is that?"

"I'm not really sure," Walt explains. "I think he figures it's not something we should be spending a lot of time on."

"Have you laid it out for him the way you just laid it out for me?" I ask.

"We've tried," Duane says. "But you know Wayne. He figures we should be out fixing machines, not developing systems that teach people how to fix them themselves."

Once again, Wayne has presented himself as a roadblock.

"I'll tell you what," I offer. "I'll talk to Wayne for you. In the meantime, you work out the details on this new development program and plan to give a presentation to all of our managers next Wednesday. Can you do that?"

"No problem," Duane says enthusiastically. "We'll be ready."

As I walk away, I suspect they'll be presenting to fewer managers than they think.

CHAPTER 26

Next stop is Melissa's. The more I think about these proposed changes, the greater sense of urgency I feel. It's time to act! Melissa's at her desk.

"Got a minute?" I ask, tapping lightly on her door.

"Sure. Come on in."

I walk in and close the door.

"I've got a whole list of things I want to talk to you about," I continue. "Maybe I should have asked for more like an hour."

"Don't worry about it. What's on your mind?"

"Big changes," I say softly. "Really big changes."

"Like what?" Melissa's eyes are fixed on mine.

"To begin with, I'm planning to let Wayne and Steve go."

Melissa doesn't blink.

"When?"

"As soon as we can put together a severance package," I explain. "Preferably tonight. I want to beat the rumormill."

"I can put a package together immediately. What kind of severance are we talking about?"

"Two weeks pay for each year of service." I state coldly. "How's that sound to you?"

"I think it's generous," she replies.

"Yeah, I figure it gives Wayne about forty weeks of pay and benefits and Steve about eighteen weeks. I'd also like to offer them some kind of outplacement assistance."

"Any preference on who we use?"

"Nah. You can choose the outplacement firm."

"Good. I've got an excellent one in mind. A friend of mine just went through it, and she swears by it."

"Just make sure you clearly define the parameters. I don't want Wayne hanging out in some cush office for the next two years."

"What kind of limits are we talking about?"

"Six months maximum. No bells and whistles."

"I'll put the letters together right away. You'll have them within an hour."

"Thanks, I appreciate that."

Melissa stares at me.

"You okay?"

"Yeah. I just feel sorry it had to come to this."

"What are you going to do about replacing them?"

"I'm not going to replace them," I reply. "We're going to absorb the losses- for now, at least."

"How are we going to do that? These are two of the most critical roles in the company."

"I understand that. But we're redesigning the company, remember? That means we're going to rethink everything we do."

"No wonder you wanted more time," she says. "I think I need to hear you explain this."

During the next fifteen minutes, I update Melissa on some of the proposals I've collected throughout the day. I begin by explaining how we intend to merge Product Development and Tool Design with Sales to improve our selling process. This gives our customers direct access to people who understand our capabilities from the inside out. They understand our products, and they understand our manufacturing processes. In theory, we actually become an extension of our customers' design process - feeding them with ideas on how to improve their performance and optimize their results. We no longer sell parts. We sell innovative and cost effective solutions.

I also explain Jim's plan to absorb the loss of Steve. Not only does this leave us with an immediate and more competent replacement, but we eliminate a high salaried position. Clearly, we can invest this money in more value-added activity.

Next, I explain Duane's new role as Process Engineering Manager, reporting directly to the Plant Manager. These functions belong together. The Plant Manager has to be accountable for more than just pumping out parts. He has to be responsible for keeping the equipment up and running efficiently, maintaining the tooling, controlling the quality of throughput, developing the people, redesigning the production processes to improve productivity and, of course, making money.

I also explain how I plan to put Roger in charge of Production Control. This gives us a command and control center that monitors everything moving through our plant, from the quality of raw materials coming in to the quality of finished products going out. It also gives us a better connection with our outside vendors and customers, since both Mark and Nancy will initially report to Roger.

Nancy will serve as our internal link to the customer. Ultimately, she'll oversee Orders, Scheduling and Shipping. By uniting these three traditional functions under Roger, we'll be giving our customers more competent and expedient service. Anytime they have a question on where an order is in our system, Nancy's team will have the answer.

Our order takers and schedulers will ultimately become cross-trained, interchangeable service representatives. We'll build a ladder for them just like Walt and Duane are doing for Production and the Trades. They'll be given an opportunity to learn more about our production processes, mold changes, machine utilization and the cost of downtime. Right now, their ignorance in these areas is causing us all kinds of problems.

Internally, we'll identify our Shipping area as the equivalent of our customers' Receiving areas. Every week, Roger and Nancy will generate a report card on the quality and service coming out of the plant and on the status of our inventories. The plant will be accountable to Production Control.

Mark will handle all procurement activity. He'll buy and inspect the materials we need on a "just-in-time" basis, he'll store them, and he'll authorize payment for them. To keep things in check, Mark will be accountable for all costs, including inventory, of incoming materials. Every month, Mark will publish a financial statement on all of our procurement activity.

Finally, I explain how in each situation we'll be building on our strengths and giving our people sound mentors. Jim brings a wealth of knowledge to our Sales Reps and Product Engineers. Duane does the same for our Process Technicians, Mechanics, Electricians, Tooling Specialists and Production Operators. And Roger ties things together beautifully between Procurement, Quality Control, Scheduling, Customer Service and Shipping.

"What about Wayne?" Melissa asks. "Who's going to run the plant?"

I smile and lean back in my chair.

"You're looking at him."

"You? How are you going to do that?"

"It's a matter of priority," I explain. "I'll find a way."

Melissa shakes her head.

"What about Bill?"

"Bill will continue in his current role, although he's making some changes to give himself more time. And he'll probably have to absorb a few of my responsibilities as G.M. while I take over as Plant Manager."

"And Q.A.?"

"We're looking at Marjorie for Q.A.," I reply. "Although, nothing's been said yet, so keep that one under your hat."

Melissa smiles. She and Marjorie are close friends.

"Can I ask what Corporate thinks about all this?"

"Well, you know Wesley," I reply. "As long as I produce results, he keeps his distance."

"In other words, he doesn't know anything about it," Melissa laughs.

"You're right," I admit. "And I've decided not to tell him until it's already in place. We'll let the results speak for themselves."

"Isn't that a little risky?" Melissa probes.

"Yeah, it probably is," I say, thinking back to Jordan's comments about high performance leaders. "Originally, I was going to put together a detailed plan for Wesley outlining all of these changes. But rather than ask for permission, I want to take the lead on this. It's the right thing to do, and I'm willing to live with the consequences. The last thing I need right now is Corporate coming down here and second guessing everything. It's time for action." I take a deep breath. "Besides, these are the kinds of changes that even Wesley will rave about."

"Let's hope so," Melissa smiles. "So I suppose you want to hear about some of the changes we plan to make in Human Resources?"

"You read my mind," I reply. "How about just a quick summary? You can cover the details at our meeting next Wednesday."

"Okay. You already know about our new Performance Management System. We'll be ready to present that next week.

We're also working with Duane and Walt and Ben on this new Employee Development Program. And you already know about that. I'm also talking to some people about setting up a new Staffing procedure. Basically, it moves us from a "pass the buck" system to an integrated, team approach to hiring. Each department will be responsible for making its own hiring decisions."

"That's putting accountability where it belongs," I say.

"Exactly. We'll still do all the recruiting and screening, but there will have to be a consensus among the hiring manager, at least one co-worker, and a Human Resources rep before we hire anybody. And we'll be screening people using our new guiding principles, not just technical know-how."

"Sounds good. Anything else?"

"Yeah, we've already begun a vigorous cross-training program in H.R. so that our people can cover for one another. And we're eliminating a lot of duplicate work."

"Like what?"

"Like benefits administration," she explains. "We've discovered that we're doing a lot of things our insurance carriers should be doing. So I'm putting an end to that immediately."

"What will you do with the extra time?" I ask.

"First, we're going to concentrate on offering more training and development. We're really weak here. Second, we'll be spending a lot more time in the plant." Melissa pauses. "In fact, I'm thinking about moving Maxine out there permanently."

I laugh. Maxine is one of our Human Resource Administrators. She gets along great with the people and handles most of our plant hiring and benefits administration. Placing her out in the plant is clearly a sign of genuine, proactive service.

"You mean have her report to the Plant Manager?"

Melissa smiles.

"I don't see why not. She's dedicated to serving the plant

anyway. And it frees me up to concentrate more on our future activity."

I stand up to leave.

"That's excellent, Melissa! She can move out there with me."

"Oh yeah," Melissa adds. "There's one more thing."

I nod.

"I'd like to rename this the 'People Department.' If you ask me, Human Resources sounds too clinical and impersonal."

Not to mention normal, I think to myself. Now there's a change I never expected to hear from Melissa.

"Call it whatever you want," I say, heading for the door. "Just make sure it reflects our mission statement and guiding principles."

CHAPTER 27

By the time I get back to my office, most of the day is shot. What started out as a brief meeting with Melissa's team turned out to be an adventuresome day of fact-finding and brainstorming. For the first time in my career, I feel like I'm actually leading people rather than managing them. They're telling me what to do, rather than the other way around. I'm pulling instead of pushing. It's just like Jordan said, "Help people to see the value in change and they may surprise you."

The meeting I've called for next Wednesday should be fascinating. There will be several powerful proposals presented - each focusing on revitalizing TYPCO into a high performance work environment. To help clear my mind, I decide to organize my thoughts on paper. I begin by sketching a new organizational chart, identifying only the people affected by the changes.

NEW ORGANIZATIONAL CHART

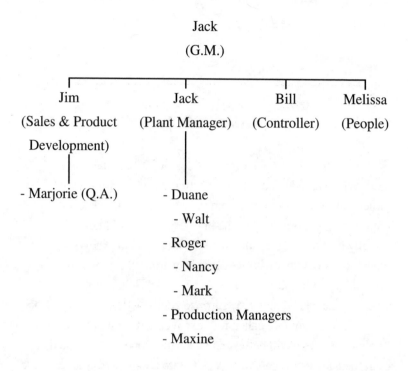

Jack

(G.M.)

Jim	Jack	Bill	Melissa
(Sales & Product Development)	(Plant Manager)	(Controller)	(People)

- Marjorie (Q.A.)

- Duane
  - Walt
- Roger
  - Nancy
  - Mark
- Production Managers
- Maxine

When I finish, I pull out a copy of our current organizational chart to compare differences. Immediately, I see a reduction in functional silos, a major shift in accountability, and more integration between tasks. Clearly, our new structure aims to break down walls and optimize our core processes.

CURRENT ORGANIZATIONAL CHART

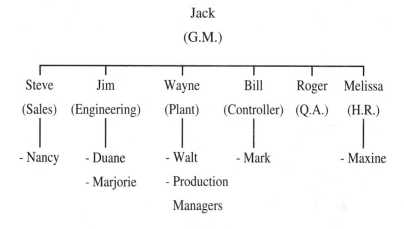

Jack

(G.M.)

Steve	Jim	Wayne	Bill	Roger	Melissa
(Sales)	(Engineering)	(Plant)	(Controller)	(Q.A.)	(H.R.)
- Nancy	- Duane	- Walt	- Mark		- Maxine
	- Marjorie	- Production Managers			

I then detail the changes I see coming.

PROPOSED CHANGES:

1. I take over temporarily as Plant Manager
2. Bill absorbs some of my responsibilites as G.M.
3. Jim takes over as Sales and Product Development Manager.
4. Marjorie reports to Jim as our new Q.A. Manager
5. Duane reports to me as Process Engineering Manager
6. Walt reports to Duane as Skilled Trades Manager
7. Roger reports to me as Production Control Manager
8. Nancy reports to Roger as Order Processing Manager
9. Mark reports to Roger as Procurement Manager
10. I evaluate Duane and Roger as potential Plant Managers.
11. Maxine reports to me as our Plant "People" Representative.
12. We decentralize our lab.
13. We institute vigorous cross-training and employee development programs

14. We reopen our labor agreement to create a few proactive, cross-functional classifications for people who want to develop new skills and add more value
15. We introduce new peer assessments to measure the quality of our internal service
16. We declutter and rename the Human Resources Department
17. We introduce team hiring
18. We move to a quarterly closing, which gives us more time in Accounting to educate and track the plant's performance
19. We design new, standardized costing and budgeting systems
20. We begin measuring the quality of our leadership

When I complete my list, I grab a copy of our guiding principles from the corner of my desk. Perusing the twelve items we now use to define our character, I begin to feel as if a great weight is being lifted from my shoulders. We're actually beginning to "walk our talk."

Our first principle reminds us to think like the customer. By uniting Sales and Product Development, and by giving our customers direct access to our Production Control Center, we will no doubt improve the quality of our service and, ultimately, begin to hear them rave.

Our second principle advises us to work cooperatively as a team. By reengineering some of our traditional silos into integrated processes, and by training our people cross-functionally, we're sure to achieve more synergistic results.

Our third principle requires that we share information with people and keep them better informed. By positioning people closer together and tracking our performance in more relevent ways, and by improving our information systems to give people better access to the score, we will remove excuses and empower people to stand on their own two feet.

Our fourth principle insists that we commit to excellence and on-going improvement. By holding all of our people accountable for quality, and by giving them mentors to learn from, we will clearly be a better company tomorrow than we are today.

Our fifth principle reminds us to be honest. In my mind, this is as honest as we've ever been - with our people and with ourselves.

Our sixth principle tells us to be consistent. By forming teams to write and implement S.O.P.'s, and by using these procedures to guide our behavior, we will improve communication and become better organized.

Our seventh principle advises us to involve people in decisions that impact their work. By inviting people to write S.O.P.'s, and by soliciting their feedback on the quality of our service, we will build the organization around our producers.

Our eighth principle calls for listening with an open mind. By implementing these changes, and by soliciting input more proactively, we will continue to discover new opportunities that move us in the direction of our mission statement.

Our ninth principle requires that we treat people with dignity, build their self-esteem and seek ways to help them achieve their potential. By creating some new cross-functional classifications, and by giving people the incentive and support to grow as individuals and as professionals, we will no doubt cultivate a winning attitude.

Our tenth principle reminds us to tolerate honest mistakes. By defining our mission and guiding principles, we can now distinguish honest mistakes from deliberate acts of destruction. Going forward, we will reward initiative that moves us in the direction of our mission, and we will confront any obstacles that stand in our way.

Our eleventh principle requires that we hold people accountable for their actions. By reengineering many of our conventional systems and realigning our reporting relationships, we will concentrate on putting accountability where it belongs. We will make sure that people have the information and resources they need to perform their work successfully, and we will track their performance accordingly.

I stop and stare at our twelveth principle. There in bold letters I read "PULL THE WEEDS". I reflect on something Roger said earlier. Removing Wayne will be the single most powerful action you can do to demonstrate your commitment to our guiding principles. Then I think about Wayne and Annette and all the fun we've had over the years. I swallow hard. Jordan insisted that I think in terms of the unit. Wayne and Steve are obstacles to our advancement. There is no doubt about what I have to do. If I'm going to lead effectively, I have no choice but to honor this principle. Our integrity - my integrity - is on the line.

There's a knock at the door. Melissa has the separation packages.

"Here's what you were looking for," she says, walking into my office. "Good luck."

"Thanks, Melissa."

"Anything else you need?" she asks.

"As a matter of fact, yes," I reply. "Could you set up a brief meeting with all of our managers and supervisors for tomorrow morning? I'd like to explain this to them in person."

"No problem. Is 8:00am okay?"

"That's fine," I say, looking over the packages. "The sooner, the better. And if anyone asks, just tell them it has to do with reengineering our culture."

"I'll see you in the morning then." Melissa turns and walks away.

I drift back over to my chair and plop down. Spinning toward the window, I catch a glimpse of a glorious sunset off to the West -

hues of brilliant oranges and reds and magentas exploding from a yellow horizon. Suddenly, I find myself analyzing Jordan's multi-dimensional organization chart. So our plant revolves around our customers, just like the earth revolves around the sun. That makes sense. We can't survive without our customers. Yet, how long did it take for humankind to discover this truth? And how many organization's still behave like they are the center of the universe? It certainly appears as if the sun crosses the earth's sky. Suddenly, I feel like an ancient explorer - about to embark on a bold and adventuresome journey.

I sigh and glance at my watch. It's almost 5:00pm. I know Wayne will be around until at least 6:00pm. Steve, on the other hand, is like greased lightning. There's no sense in procrastinating. It's time to do some gardening.

I grab the separation packages and head for the door. *The revolution has begun.*

PART VII

Count Your Blessings

Epilogue

"Welcome aboard, Kevin!" Jordan says as my son steps onto the magnificent sloop. "You ready to take on the Atlantic?"

"Yeah," my son replies. "I've been looking forward to this for a long time."

"Good. There's nothing like working in harmony with Mother Nature."

"How fast does this boat go?" Kathleen asks, taking Jordan's hand and climbing aboard.

"That all depends, Kathleen," the man replies. "What do you say we find out together?"

"So this is Jordan McKay?" my wife says, grabbing Jordan's hand and climbing aboard. "I've heard so many good things about you."

"Well, your husband is a gifted man, Judy. And it takes a gifted person to make any sense out of what I say."

Judy and I both laugh.

"C'mon up here, Nick," Jordan hollers to the galley below. "Our guests have arrived."

Seconds later, a beautiful suntanned face appears at the top of the ladder emerging from the galley. Nicole McKay climbs out of the forward hatch and smiles radiantly as she stretches out her hand.

"Good morning," she says softly. "It's nice to finally meet

you."

Following a round of formal introductions, Nicole leads my wife down to the galley to store the overabundance of food we have in tow, while Kevin and Kathleen head toward the bow of the 42-foot craft.

"So this is the boat I keep hearing about," I say, looking it over.

"You only hear about it because you haven't been on it yet," Jordan replies. "Now that you've accepted my invitation, you can judge it for yourself."

"And if it sinks?" I quip.

"Then I trust your perception will differ from mine. If you like, we can just motor around the harbor," he jokes.

"What do you guys think?" I shout to the kids. "Do you want to play it safe and just motor around the harbor?"

"No way, Dad!" they both scream simultaneously. "Let's go out and look for some whales!"

"Sounds like a consensus," Jordan confirms. "What do you say we get underway?"

Minutes later, we've eased effortlessly out of the slip, and we are maneuvering our way toward the mouth of the harbor. Jordan is at the helm and I'm climbing back into the cockpit after releasing the stern lines. The kids are sitting up on the bow, scanning the faces along the shore, and teasing a crafty gull dancing in the wind just out of their reach. In the distance, the mighty Atlantic awaits us.

"So fill me," Jordan prompts. "I'm eager to hear how you've progressed during the past few months."

"It's been remarkable," I reply. "Since we met a year ago, our culture has changed dramatically. It's like our division has a whole new personality."

"And how would you describe this personality?" he probes.

"Maybe character is a better word for it," I explain. "In any case, we're more connected and interactive. We're more imaginative. We're more responsive. We're more sensitive to one another's needs. Our managers are learning to lead, and our people are learning to manage themselves. We know where we're going and we're all moving in the same direction."

"That's encouraging," Jordan says. "And the parameters are in place to guide people as they move in this direction?"

"We're still developing and refining certain procedures to facilitate what we're doing, but the ones we have in place are working beautifully. And they're all in harmony with our guiding principles."

"And the people are committed to them?"

"They wrote them," I respond. "And we both know that people are less likely to argue with their own data."

The agent of change smiles.

"And you know for a fact that your managers are leading people by gaining their commitment?" he asks.

"It's one of our semi-annual measurements," I reply. "We've learned that you get what you inspect, not what you expect."

Jordan smiles again.

"I'm impressed, Jack," he says. "And I'll bet your people are becoming more confident in taking responsibility and making decisions?"

"Maslow would be proud," I quip.

This time he laughs.

"Do you still feel like you're suffering from employee dependency syndrome?" he quizzes.

"On the contrary," I answer. "I now spend the majority of my time wandering around asking questions, listening and observing. The people are taking the lead and I'm doing my own personal assessment of their commitment."

"Very good. And what kind of questions are you asking?"

"Think about it," I state boldly. "I'll bet you can figure it out." Jordan laughs again.

"How about your labor contract?" he continues. "The last time we talked you were in the middle of some renegotiations."

"The negotiations went very well," I reply. "We created four new classifications - one in Technical Services and three in Production."

"And these classifications merge several other classifications together?" he probes.

"That's right," I answer. "They give people a chance to earn more money by cross-training and cross-utilizing their skills. It works like an apprenticeship program for all of our people. Ultimately, we'll have fewer classifications, but each classification will offer several levels for advancement. Anyone interested in advancing their skills has the opportunity and incentive to do so. The new arrangement stimulates continuous learning - one of our guiding principles."

"And what kind of response are you getting from it?"

"The day we offered it, we had almost 40% of our people sign up," I reply. "Of course, not all of them were qualified to move into some of the more advanced levels immediately, but we were able to start setting some meaningful goals."

"Who established the criteria on how to qualify people for the specific levels within a classification?"

"We put a cross-functional team together to define the criteria for each stage," I reply. "Once the criteria was defined, we had the team develop testing for each stage and then we added financial incentives."

"So you have teams doing a lot more than just purchasing new equipment and conducting audits?" Jordan smiles.

This time I laugh.

"That seems like such a long, long time ago," I say. "It's hard to believe how fast the past 12 months have gone.

"I trust that means you've come a long, long way," Jordan adds.

"There's no doubt about that," I confirm. "Even my boss up at Corporate is raving about us. In fact, we've become a pilot operation for the entire company. We have people coming in almost every week now to study us. They all want to know how we did it."

"I take it your numbers paint a healthy picture?"

"You better believe it!," I rave. "We've cut our inventories in half. Our lead times are down 40%. Our machine downtime is down 50%. Our customer reported defects are down 90%. Our scrap rate is down 20%. And our employment is down 5%, mostly through attrition, even though our business is up 15%. As a matter of fact, we just signed a three-year, multi-million dollar contract with Peak Performance, a customer who was threatening to leave us eight months ago."

"Sounds productive."

"And our earnings look better than ever. Like I said, even Corporate is raving about us."

"What about some of the management changes? How did people react to that?"

"Wayne's departure was a shocker. Even Corporate was surprised. But, in retrospect, it was clearly the right thing to do. People respected the decision and it created vast opportunity for the people who remain at TYPCO. It's like you said. It was best for the unit as a whole."

"Do you still talk to Wayne at all?"

"Not recently. He doesn't return any of my phone calls, and I don't push it much. I guess I can't really blame him for being bitter."

"And Steve?"

"Steve just disappeared. Quite frankly, I was a little surprised at how passive he was about the whole thing. My gut tells me that he knew he was in over his head anyway. We probably did him a favor."

"What about Nancy and Mark? How are they doing?"

"At first, they were both a little disappointed about reporting to Roger. That was before they discovered how helpful Roger can be without Wayne around. He's done an outstanding job grooming both of them for additional responsibilities."

"Good for Roger."

"They were also a little ticked off at me about where they fit on the new organizational chart."

"I'm not surprised."

"Of course, when they saw where I fit in the new structure, they both realized they were barking up an empty tree. Not to mention, they both got healthy raises to compensate for their increased responsibilities."

"And now?"

"Now they're turning the place upside down. Between Roger, Mark, Nancy and Duane, I couldn't ask for a better manufacturing team. They're breathing new life into the company everyday."

"So are you still filling the role of Plant Manager?"

"Only temporarily," I explain. "But I'm planning to have our Production Managers begin reporting to Duane in another month. So technically, he'll handle all of Production and Process Engineering, while Roger will continue to oversee Production Control."

"So Roger isn't going to be your Plant Manager?"

"No. You were right about Roger. He's better suited for what he's doing now. Everything's really starting to fall into place."

"I'll attest to that," Judy interjects, climbing out of the galley with Nicole following her. "Including my husband."

"Well, speaking of falling into place, who wants to take the helm while I get these sails up?" Jordan asks.

"I'm ready when you are, Skipper," Judy volunteers.

"Good," the captain replies. "Just take the wheel and keep her pointed steady into the wind."

"What do you want me to do?" I ask.

"Stop talking about work," Jordan replies. "You'll bore our new skipper."

Judy laughs.

"No, you won't," she says. "I'm really interested in what you two have been doing. In fact, we could use your help at the hospital."

"Do you work with any hospitals, Jordan?" I ask.

"As a matter of fact, I do," he replies. "Especially, these days. This whole health care reform movement has me stretching in multiple directions."

"Well, I'm sure a lot of people can use your help," Judy says. "If anything needs to be reengineered, it's this country's health care system."

"Not to mention our government," I add. "I just wonder how things get so out of control."

"It's no different than it is in your business, Jack," Jordan huffs, as he quickly cranks the halyard hoisting the flapping main sail. "Most people lose sight of the big picture. They confuse activity with productivity. Without a clear vision of what we're ultimately trying to achieve, we tend to focus our activity on what we assume is correct. And if our assumptions are flawed, our activity is often irrelevent." He stops and locks the main sail into place. "Most people do not dare to be different. They do not question why they do certain things, and even when they do, their answers are often skewed by some precedent or societal norm. This leads to a lot of activity and clutter that, in the long run, doesn't really matter."

"It also creates the need to stop and rethink our methods once in a while," I add. "People do tend to get sidetracked."

"It certainly was true in my case," Jordan admits, jumping back into the cockpit and looking over at Nicole. "Until we reengineered our own lifestyle, that is."

Judy and I both look at him with surprise. Nicole smiles.

"What do you mean?" I probe.

Jordan stops what he is doing momentarily and turns to me.

"This may come as a shock to you, Jack, but I haven't always practiced what I now preach," he explains. "I used to think that I was invulnerable. My goal was to be the best at everything I did. Quite frankly, I was a lousy loser. I wanted power and control and wealth. This was my definition of success. By age 29, I was General Manager of a division about the size of yours. I had an excellent education, and I was making a ton of money. I was learning something new every day. I had a great wife and a beautiful son. My life was filled with accomplishments and dreams yet to be realized. Tomorrow was always going to be a better day than today."

"So what happened?" I ask.

"Think about it while I get the Genoa ready," he replies.

Jordan hops out of the cockpit and heads toward the bow of the boat.

"Your husband is an enigma, Nicole," I laugh. "Just when I think I have him figured out, he throws me a curve ball."

"You might be surprised," she replies softly. "He's really quite a simple man."

As I observe Nicole, I begin to sense a very wise woman. She's tuned into what's going on, but reluctant to say much without being asked. Once questioned, however, she speaks with gentle confidence and poise. Her words are crafted carefully and presented with dignity. Her smile reveals a personality that is vivid and full of life, yet never overbearing. Her hazel-green eyes dance back and forth, scanning for truth, while her tone remains warm and welcoming. This woman is complete. Her internal beauty reinforces that of her stunning exterior. Somehow, she has mastered the art of bringing mind, body and soul together in harmony.

"And how is that?" I ask.

"You tell me, Jack," Nicole responds. "What has Jordan *really* taught you?"

Suddenly, I feel like I'm right back where I started. Nicole quizzes me in the same way Jordan does. My mind races to the lessons and the legacy Jordan has left behind in my world. Where do I even begin?

"I think I can answer that," Judy pipes in. "Jordan has taught Jack to focus on the things that matter most, and to redefine his priorities and objectives under a very different paradigm."

"And what is that paradigm?" Nicole asks.

"That in order to be rich, one must enrich others," Judy replies. "And in order to gain power, one must learn to empower others."

I couldn't have said it any better.

"And have you discovered this to be true, Jack?" Nicole continues.

"Without a doubt," I confirm. "Both at work and at home."

"I'll second that," Judy adds.

"And do you consider this complicated?" Nicole smiles.

"Complicated? No. Misunderstood? Yes. Abused? Definitely."

"It's like I said, Jordan is really a rather simple man."

"So when Jordan was talking about being in search of power and control and wealth - are you saying he was wrong?"

"On the contrary," Nicole replies. "These are worthwhile goals many people aspire to. We simply learned that achieving these objectives alone does not ensure enrichment and happiness, especially if they are achieved at the expense of others. Jordan said that his life was filled with dreams yet to be realized - that tomorrow was going to be better than today."

"What's wrong with that?" I ask.

"Under that mindset, tomorrow never comes," Nicole explains. "It always remains out of reach."

"So despite remarkable accomplishments, a person can become trapped with a feeling of unhappiness and dissatisfaction," I add.

"That's what we discovered," Jordan interjects, leaping back into the cockpit. "I had become my own worst enemy. First, it was ten-hour days, six days a week. Then it was twelve-hour days. Then it became seven day weeks. Soon, the more money we made, the more we acquired - but the less time we had to enjoy it. By age 35, I was president of a large company and we were acquiring new companies as quickly as we could snatch them up. This put me on the road extensively. But I had convinced myself that "tomorrow" Nicole and I would be together again - that somehow tomorrow we would make up for today. And that tomorrow I would be there for my son. Unfortunately, tomorrow never came and years were passing us by - years I could never recapture with the people I most loved. I finally learned that all of the money and power in the world could not buy me another tomorrow. I had to learn to cherish today."

"That sounds familiar," I add.

"So what changed all of this?" Judy asks.

Jordan looks over at Nicole.

"A question," he says. "Actually, a series of questions."

"Beginning with what?" I ask.

"Beginning with 'How do I want to be remembered?'"

"That's an interesting question," Judy replies.

"And an easy one to overlook," Jordan adds. "At least, in my case it was. Like many of my peers, I was caught up in a race I could not win because there was no end to the race. Long after I was gone, the race would continue on and I would be forgotten."

"So you discovered that life is not a game?" I poke, using the same analogy Jordan had used with me.

"That's exactly right," Jordan responds earnestly. "And I was treating it like it was a game to be won."

"You mentioned a series of questions," Judy interjects. "What other questions did you ask?"

"Well, once I began thinking about how I wanted to be remembered, I had to begin answering questions focusing on my own personal mission statement and guiding principles. I had to know my purpose and define my character. Next, I had to understand my true competition and challenge my own assumptions. Finally, I had to confront my fears and plug myself into the new equation. You see, Jack, what I have shared with you is something I had to first learn and master myself - both individually and as the president of a large company."

"And you say this began at age 35?" I ask.

"I remember the day as if it were yesterday," Jordan answers solemnly.

"So do I," Nicole whispers, leaning over and putting her arm around her partner.

"What happened?" Judy asks curiously.

"It was the day our son John was taken from us," Jordan says quietly, the wind blowing through his hair. "You see, I had to learn this lesson the hard way. Tomorrow never came for John and me."

ABOUT THE AUTHOR

John Murphy is founder and president of Venture Management Consultants, Inc., a firm specializing in creating high performance work environments. As a practitioner of these principles, John advises organizations worldwide on how to break through many of the conventional paradigms that stand in the way of real progress.

Prior to consulting, John headed Corporate Human Resources for the American division of Paulstra, an international automotive supplier based in Paris, France. While with Paulstra, John helped implement many of the concepts presented in this book, leading to dramatic improvements in quality, service, productivity and employee morale.

John is a graduate of the University of Notre Dame and the University of Michigan Graduate Business School's Human Resource Executive Program.

ACKNOWLEDGMENTS

This book is dedicated to all of the "agents of change" in my life - the people who have expanded my horizons by opening my mind and senses to the vast opportunities that await those who persevere. To me, these are the real heroes in the world today. They have spanned the globe for centuries gracing us with inspiring acts of decency and empowering words of wisdom. Some of them are still alive today. Others died as many as 2000 years ago. Needless to say, their impact can be measured by the legacy they've left behind.

Closer to home, I wish to acknowledge my wife, Stephanie, and our four precious children. Their presence has helped me to see the world from a much broader perspective, giving me invaluable insight on how to apply the principles addressed in this book.

I also want to acknowledge my parents and six brothers and sisters. Your guidance and support, along with your diverse interests and points of view, have instilled in me a much greater sense of purpose and character. I have always felt that I wouldn't be quite the same without each one of you.

Professionally, I wish to acknowledge Jean Pierre Serra. Your leadership, along with your Socratic style, has challenged me to think differently about the way an organization can operate. I will never forget the powerful lessons you helped me discover - and understand.

Finally, I wish to acknowledge all of the people - my dear friends - who helped me put this book together. This includes Meredith Gremel, John Massey, Michael Walsh, Michael Armstrong, Elizabeth Jennings, David Murphy, Ted Gedra, Andy Gremel and Richard Murphy. Thank you for your encouragement, dedication and support.

For more information on how John Murphy can help
your organization, or to order John's other books,
call 1-800-942-1120.